FLEMING
Discoverer of Penicillin

Sir Alexander Fleming in his laboratory

FLEMING

Discoverer of Penicillin

by

L. J. LUDOVICI

" A very perfit practisour : the cause once
knowen and the right measure, anon he
gave the sike man his cure."

Chaucer (*Canterbury Tales*).

BLOOMINGTON
INDIANA UNIVERSITY PRESS

First published October, 1952
Reprinted October, 1952

Printed in Great Britain
at the BURLEIGH PRESS, *Lewins Mead*, BRISTOL

For M.L. who knows the reason why, and
for R.E.L. who will one day know the
reason why . . .
And for J.L., M.L., Dr. H.L. and E.L.,
only true survivors of the clan, who also
matter very much . . .

ACKNOWLEDGMENTS

For the help they have so willingly given me, and for many kindnesses, I wish to express my thanks to :

SIR ALEXANDER FLEMING

MR. ROBERT J. FLEMING

DR. LEONARD COLEBROOK

PROFESSOR CHARLES A. PANNETT

DR. DAVID W. CARMALT JONES

MISS MARY G. MILNE

MISS MARJORIE PEGRAM

MISS P. N. HUNTER

MR. RONALD GRAY and MR. ROBIN BAILES who also gave me much help are now dead, but I here wish to remember their great kindness.

CONTENTS

CHAP.   PAGE

   I. Alpha and Omega - - - - - - 11

  II. Boyhood at Lochfield - - - - - 18

 III. The Classroom, The City, St. Mary's - 24

 IV. The Challenge of Medical Research - 33

  V. The Fledgling Bacteriologist - - - 41

 VI. First Discoveries - - - - - - 51

 VII. The Boulogne Days : 1914–1918 - - - 66

VIII. Scepticism and Activity - - - - 82

 IX. The Precursor of Penicillin - - - 94

  X. The Natural Defences of the Body - - 108

 XI. The Great Scientist - - - - - 122

 XII. The Winds of Heaven - - - - - 131

XIII. Penicillin : The Evil of Waiting - - 154

XIV. Palmam qui meruit ferat - - - - 173

 XV. A Whole New World of Science - - 185

XVI. The Light of Renown - - - - - 198

XVII. " . . . the flavour of youth " - - - 210

      Bibliography - - - - - - - 215

      Index - - - - - - - - 221

ix

ILLUSTRATIONS

SIR ALEXANDER FLEMING IN HIS LABORATORY - *Frontispiece*

WITH SIR ALMROTH WRIGHT - - - *facing page* 112

DIFFERENTIAL INHIBITION OF BACTERIA BY
PENICILLIN AND LYSOZYME EMBEDDED IN A
GUTTER IN AN AGAR PLATE - - ,, ,, 113

ARRIVING AT LE BOURGET TO BE HONOURED BY
THE PARIS *Académie de Médicine*. FLEMING
WITH THE DISTINGUISHED FRENCH SCIEN-
TISTS (left to right) VALLERY-RADOT,
TREFOUELS AND LEPINE - - - - ,, ,, 128

RECEIVING THE CONGRATULATIONS OF ONE OF
THE FIRST AMERICAN FIRMS TO PRODUCE
PENICILLIN COMMERCIALLY - - - ,, ,, 129

ALPHA AND OMEGA

THE TIDES of respectability flowing through the Paddington
district of London are on the ebb before they reach Praed
Street. At the western extremity of Praed Street stands the
Paddington railway terminus, and within sound of the hiss
and clatter of arriving and departing trains stretches the
façade of St. Mary's Hospital, whose stolid, red-brick mass
forms an enduring presence among the shifting fortunes of a
drab and congested thoroughfare, given over to an infinite
variety of commerce both licit and illicit.

Few passers-by, however, spare more than a casual glance
at the extensive frontage of St. Mary's. Even fewer seem
aware that behind its walls, separating the world of the
hospital from the raw and restless world outside, men of
science have toiled and discovered remedies for hitherto
incurable ills of the flesh.

Yet even two such antipathetic worlds are lightly linked by
humorous legend. It is said that the mould spore which
floated high above Praed Street and came to rest in Dr.
Alexander Fleming's Petri dish, thereby providing the genesis
of penicillin, had detached itself from an old beer barrel in
a near-by public house much frequented by St. Mary's men.
A reporter with a carefree imagination and a sublime dis-
regard for chronology asserted that, " we owe penicillin to the
German who dropped a bomb close to the bacteriological
laboratory of St. Mary's Hospital. The convulsion caused the
local *Penicillium notatum* to permeate into the glass tubes in
which gelatine or agar is kept, which substance houses the
deadliest of germs. All these valuable germs died."

Fleming's comment upon this enthralling confection is terse :
" He was twelve years too late ; penicillin was discovered in
1928."

Another journal went one better. According to it : " Sir
Archibald (!) Fleming, that great scientist, is such a busy man

that he has no time to go out for lunch. He takes sandwiches with him and eats them while at work in his laboratory. Being overworked and run down, he developed some nasty boils, but unable to take a rest he went on working. One day he was so busy that he did not notice that he took up the wrong packet of sandwiches until he had finished eating them. They were a fortnight old and green with mould. A curious result followed, his boils disappeared. He then realized that mould could act as a medicine and that is how penicillin was discovered."

"It was a religious paper so it must be true" remarks Fleming concerning this fiction of his absent-mindedness.

So much for fancy. The fact was that the preparation of Fleming's mind for one of the most auspicious observations in the whole history of medical research had begun in the days of horse-buses and hansom-cabs, of the frills and furbelows of the Edwardian mode. Already in 1906 he belonged to a group of young doctors who daily turned out of Praed Street and passed into St. Mary's Hospital to work under the guidance of a man whose ideas had lit fires in their minds.

That man was Almroth Wright.

When he arrived at St. Mary's in 1902, Wright was already great in science, for he had successfully introduced preventive inoculation against typhoid using killed vaccines. "Pasteur" says Fleming, "had once and for all established the principle of prophylactic inoculation against infective disease, but he had used *living* vaccines in his work. This was possible in treating animals but it was not, owing to certain risks, suitable for the treatment of humans. The introduction of *killed* vaccines for the prevention and treatment of disease was largely the work of our great countryman, Sir Almroth Wright."

To young aspirants in medicine, Wright, who had a dynamic and inspiring personality, flung down an irresistible challenge by expressing his conviction that the medicine of the time was virtually an unexplored universe. "If the belief is nurtured that the medical art of to-day can effectually intervene in the course of disease" he declared, "this ought to be dismissed as an illusion." Then, as though reaching beyond brutal fact to touch open an inner door and draw upon compassion, he said : " Of all the evils which befall man in his civilized state, the evil of disease is incomparably the greatest."

Fleming and others dedicated themselves to the mitigation of that evil, moved perhaps by the same " pain in the mind " which everlastingly haunted Wright.

Certainly it was not the lure of wealth nor any distant prospect of honours which kept them at their labours from early in the morning until far into the night : day after day, month after month, year after year, Moreover, had not Pasteur stated that, " science is the graveyard of ideas ? " They were quite aware that the prizes of science were as elusive as the quicksilver which so much assists its practice, and the remuneration of medical research workers was so inadequate that Wright protested publicly about their conditions of service.

Fleming spent years studying the astonishing way in which the phagocytes or leucocytes (white cells in the body) consumed disease-microbes, leaving him with an unforgettable impression of Nature's powers. During the First World War he became interested in the action of antiseptics, and in 1922 he came upon a natural antiseptic in the body which he called lysozyme.

Strewn across a career these events might have seemed unconnected, but in retrospect they fall into their well-assigned places in a grand design. His discovery of lysozyme turned out to be the indispensable prelude to his discovery of penicillin.

Modestly Fleming says that his success rests upon pillars fortuitously constructed by chance or destiny. In his Nobel Prize Lecture, delivered in Stockholm on December 11th, 1945, he stated :

" It arose simply from a fortunate occurrence which happened when I was working on a purely academic bacteriological problem which had nothing to do with bacterial antagonism, or moulds, or antiseptics or antibiotics. In my first publication I might have claimed that I came to the conclusion as a result of serious study of the literature and deep thought, that valuable antibacterial substances were made by moulds, and that I set out to investigate the problem. That would have been untrue, and I preferred to tell the truth, that penicillin started as a chance observation.

" My only merit is that I did not neglect the observation, and that I pursued the subject as a bacteriologist."

A fortunate occurrence! A chance observation! But Pasteur held that " there are no accidents in science", that " in the fields of observation chance only favours the mind prepared."

Twenty-two years of intense, creative labour in Wright's laboratory had prepared Fleming for an apocalyptic moment.

And for those who attribute the discovery of penicillin to the mysterious operations of a Divine Providence there is an exquisite irony, since the chosen instrument of its expression was a man who was a militant disbeliever in the efficacy of antiseptics as therapeutic applications. Yet into his hands fell the opportunity of delivering to mankind the most perfect antiseptic of all, whose coming opened up new highways in research and revolutionized surgery.

" 'Tis not in mortals to command success, but we've done more, Sempronius, we've deserved it." By the time success came and the world showered its honours upon him, Fleming had well deserved it.

To-day at St. Mary's Hospital there is a doorway crowned by an inscription which reads : WRIGHT-FLEMING INSTITUTE OF MICROBIOLOGY, and this nomenclature is commemorative of two of the greatest figures in bacteriology of all time, of a notable era in the history of British medicine and in the history of human welfare. Wright assured immunity from typhoid by inoculation, and Fleming, when he discovered penicillin, exorcised the terrors of a host of afflictions.

Wright is dead, but he lived long enough to see the short, sturdy Dr. Fleming who had joined him in 1906 elected to the Royal Society in 1943, and to see him receive a knighthood in 1944.

Now in the Wright-Fleming Institute, Sir Alexander Fleming directs the activities of a sizeable team of research workers. At the end of a long corridor, a room of unassuming proportions is both laboratory and office to him. Its door is seldom closed and white-coated assistants constantly come in, consult with him and then go out again. Its very simplicity, its workaday atmosphere focus the imagination upon the inward strength of a man who has no need to serve himself of the pomp and protective paraphernalia to which an exalted position could entitle him.

Its unspectacular contents almost hesitantly reveal the important phases of an outstanding career. Topping the photographs on the wall to the right of the simple desk at which he sits in a swivel chair is a picture of Wright. Among them also is an old print of St. Mary's, and in a group Fleming is shown next to Mr. Churchill, both capped and gowned and suitably grave. The caption beneath an imposing view of the Vienna General Hospital tells how he was honoured by the Medical Society there in 1947, and in the Bateman cartoon of him is a glint of humour. It says : " The only F.R.C.S. who never did a real operation ! "

Indeed, grave and gay are nicely juxtaposed on those walls. A drawing by Ronald Gray shows Fleming in the uniform of a private soldier carrying not a gun but an immense hypodermic syringe, and in one of several magazine cartoons a delighted lady exclaims : " Oh, it was a lovely film, all about a woman living in a little town in America who discovered penicillin."

Behind him and alongside him runs his laboratory bench with its microscopes, its racks full of test-tubes ; a wall-bracket houses bottles, and the thin blue flame of a Bunsen burner carries to the nostrils the smell of coal gas, which mingles with the strange smells of other potions. One of the test-tubes is partly filled with what looks like rusty-coloured shot and rattles as it is lifted out of place. It is a pike's roe, and Fleming caught the fish and extracted the roe to prove that it contained lysozyme, the antibacterial ferment he discovered.

Facing him is a tall glass-fronted bookcase alongside which hangs a specimen of Pasteur's handwriting in its frame ; near to it is a metal shield mounted on wood and bearing the words :

VARIETY CLUBS OF AMERICA
Citation Trophy
This award of 1944 presented to Dr. Alexander Fleming with grateful appreciation of his invaluable contributions in the field of medicine.
" Inasmuch as ye have done it unto the least of these . . . ye have done it unto Me. . . . "

A bronze medallion with his head embossed upon it says : *Prix Nobel* 1945, and at one end of his laboratory bench is a statuette of a knight on horseback holding aloft a sword : " *A Sir Alexander, Fleming, Verona, 28 Iuglio 1947.*" He is a freeman of that city, famous for the palace of Scaliger.

He moves about the room with springy step, neatly dressed, wearing his usual bow-tie. A shaft of sunlight falls upon his full head of well-brushed white hair, adding a greater glow to his smooth, ruddy complexion and lighting up the startlingly blue eyes, clear and translucent. The hands are shapely, sensitive, the finger-tips square. According to his eldest sister he has his mother's eyes and his father's hands. His glance is unwavering as he talks in his soft Scottish accents, continuously smoking cigarettes. His smile illuminates his face for an instant, softens it, then gradually dissolves as mouth and chin are again set in their usual determined cast.

There are occasions when he withdraws into himself for days, when his conversation, habitually spare, becomes even sparer. Is he wrestling with that " pain in the mind " of which Wright had spoken ? Is he preoccupied with his own deep feelings, rarely displayed, the feelings of a kindly man of great sensibility moved by the tragic antics of a world he had endowed with an inestimable gift ? Speaking at the Pasteur Exhibition in 1947, he quoted certain words of the great Frenchman :—

"I would say that two contrary laws seem to be battling with each other nowadays : the one a law of blood and death, ever imagining new means of destruction and forcing nations to be constantly ready for the battlefield—the other a law of peace, work, and health, ever evolving new means of delivering man from the scourges which beset him. Which of these two laws will ultimately prevail ? God alone knows."

" How true to-day ! " added Fleming.

Yet flashing through all is the quick thrust of his wit. One day in America a journalist with a high personal interest enquired : " Say, is this penicillin of yours any good for a hang-over ? " To which Fleming immediately came back : " Heavens no, it's not that good."

If anyone asks him how to be successful he gives them the

one answer : " I would say—work, work and work again."
Devotedly he has practised what he has preached, his main
recreations found in the life of the open air to which he was
born and bred among the hills of Ayrshire.

That, however, is where his story begins.

CHAPTER II

BOYHOOD AT LOCHFIELD

AYRSHIRE IN south-western Scotland has been spoken of as a rich, sweet land with a brisk, healthy climate, across which sea-winds eternally bear whispers of the ballades of Robert Burns.

Yet the Ayrshire scene around Darvel in the Irvine Valley provokes sterner fancies. There the river is squeezed in by rising ground on both sides, and the wooded slope of Lanfine falls steadily towards this " lang toon ". A walker through its main street faces the bald summit of Loudoun Hill which, rising to a thousand and thirty-four feet, brings the valley to an end and dominates the Strathaven road beyond. About four miles northwards from Darvel and Loudoun Hill, across an undulating scene, beyond the closely cultivated lands and the jostling farms of the valley, is a wide plateau, cut through by the Glen Water and by lesser streams, like Loch Burn flowing westwards and Calder Burn flowing eastwards to join the Avon and the Clyde.

On this watershed, at an altitude of eight hundred feet, stands Lochfield Farm, a low, sturdy house in stone within the suggestion of a protective hollow on a declivity, with trees clustering about it which break the force of tempestuous winds. Indeed, it might equally well have been called World's End, for a good cart-track branching away at Laigh Bradly from the country road leading north out of Darvel finishes up at its front door. Looking down at Lochfield from a distance it appears a little island in a sea of moorland grass, for this is extensive sheep land, sparsely cultivated and sparsely inhabited.

There, amid the silence of infinite spaces, Alexander Fleming was born on August 6th, 1881. During that year Mr. Gladstone (to Queen Victoria's evident displeasure) had taken office for the second time in his marathon political career, and Disraeli had died. But more remarkable, a scientist, momentarily

deserting the isolation of his laboratory, had presented to the
world a spectacle as exciting as any that the brains of a master-
showman could contrive. At a farmyard at Pouilly-le-Fort
near Melun in France, Pasteur had demonstrated that it was
possible to secure immunity against infective disease. " Well
then ! Men of little faith ! " he had cried, triumphant, as
abashed sceptics watched the sheep he had treated with his
vaccine nibbling and chewing alongside the bodies of his
untreated controls, lying dead of anthrax. " For Pasteur,
1881 was a memorable year," Fleming has said, " so it was
for me for it was then I was born."

Alexander Fleming's father, Hugh Fleming, quitting his own
district of Strathaven further up the Irvine Valley, had rented
the eight hundred acres making up Lochfield Farm from the
Earl of Loudoun's estates. It was too high up for wheat, which
did not ripen easily, so oats were sown instead and formed the
principal grain crop. Root vegetables provided winter fodder
for the Ayrshire cattle in their pasturages. Sheep-breeding,
and especially the sale of dairy produce were the chief sources
of a reasonable livelihood.

Hugh Fleming married twice. By his first wife he had four
children : a daughter, Jean, followed by two sons, Hugh and
Thomas, and another daughter, Mary. In 1876, some time
after the death of his first wife, he married Grace Morton of
Bransfield Farm near Darvel. By her also he had four
children : a daughter, Grace, followed by three sons, John,
Robert and Alexander, who was thus the youngest of them all.

They were a family representative enough of many like
them inhabiting the Scottish countryside, farmers from time
immemorial, uninterruptedly tied to their native soil, handing
on from generation to generation the same persistent
characteristics determined by little changing conditions of life :
a profound sense of independence, tenacity, patience and
industry ; a clear-headed grasp of reality and a taciturnity
concealing a warmness of heart. Trevelyan has described
them as, " the best educated countrymen in Europe, often
plunged in solitary meditation and as often roused to furious
argument on points of logic and theology which few English-
men had the mental gifts or training to understand." Moreover,

out of a ceaseless struggle with their share of unresponsive acres and an everlasting watch upon Nature, they accumulated their own wisdoms, and braced by a tight self-discipline, confronted the whimsicalities of the weather, the quixotries of the markets and the inanition of governments repeatedly lamenting the ruin of agriculture.

Such then were the mental and moral vantages that Alexander Fleming could claim from his heritage.

Unhappily his father died in 1888, when he was still only seven. His mother was at once left to assume formidable responsibilities. She had to supervise the running of the farm, to maintain a large family and to guide their ways. It was an exacting test, but possessed of exceptional character and a harmonious and balanced temperament, she was equal to it. " She was an excellent and cheerful mother and housekeeper," says Robert of her, " and an excellent cook. She was very practical indeed, yet, when time permitted, she was always ready to join in indoor games or in any fun we were having." Certainly she always had a wholly united family about her, standing at the centre of the affections both of her own and her step-children, between whom not the smallest hint of division existed.

Now, upon her husband's death, Hugh, the oldest boy, immediately took his father's place, and aided by her counsels, managed the farm. It turned out to be his permanent avocation and in due time he bought up Lochfield, married the daughter of a farmer-neighbour he had known from childhood, and died where he had been born at the age of seventy-nine.

About two years before his father's death, Alexander had begun his schooldays. Daily, with his sister, Grace, and his brothers, John and Robert, he tramped a little over a mile across the fields and through Lochfield Glen to the low-roofed stone cottage with the squat chimneys perched at each end. This was Loudoun Moor school, a single classroom in which a succession of teachers imparted to them the rudiments of knowledge : reading, writing and arithmetic. They needed no fat register in which to enter the names of their pupils, a swift glance round was an adequate form of roll-call, for the four Flemings, four children of another family and four or five boys and girls out of various homes (" the assortments "), made up their numbers.

" My schooling," Alexander Fleming has stated, " was really in a wee school out in the country away beyond Darvel. But that wee school up on the hill, that's where they really taught you something." He continues : " The brighter part of my schooldays was when I went at the age of five to Loudoun Moor School. There were fourteen or fifteen of us. We had many teachers there ; they never stayed long, but the two I remember especially were Marion Stirling and Martha Aird, and they taught us how to read, write, spell and count, so that when we came down to the big school at Darvel we weren't disgraced."

These young teachers were as well known to the parents and their children as parents and children were well known to them. Indeed they regarded their charges as a large family, creating an easy, informal atmosphere for them, in which they could feel free to express themselves. Yet an essential dignity implied a boundary that none of the children would lightly have ventured to trespass. Alexander Fleming recounts how in later years, after the discovery of penicillin " had got my name in the papers", Marion Stirling, his first teacher, wrote from South Africa to remind him that she had taught him his first school lessons.

According to his brother, Robert, " he took easily to his lessons and never needed to apply himself to them too diligently. He certainly had an alert intelligence and excellent powers of observation but I do not think he ever bothered much about observing people. He learnt things easily even when he was a small boy." From the beginning his preoccupation was with Nature. Every spare moment of his boyhood was taken up in tramping the remote uplands surrounding Lochfield over which the black-faced sheep roamed, whose solitude was challenged by only a handful of humans. There were numberless hill-crests upon which a boy could in adventurous imagination plant a flag, the ridges between High Overmoor, through the High Alderstocks and beyond to the north, and to the south-east the Dungavel Hills running into the great ranges separating the Darvel Valley from Sorn.

Their tonic airs engulfed him, the habits of their birds and beasts enthralled him. In the late summer and early autumn, blanketed with purple heather, they knew a moment of glory ; when the snows came they were an erratic pattern of mud-browns, slate-greys and white, and in the green of springtime, when the Glen Water was in spate, foaming as it plunged over smooth-worn boulders, its less turbulent stretches in Lochfield Glen made gilded patterns in the sunshine.

Only on those Sundays when his turn came to climb into the pony trap with some of his brothers and sisters and jog into Darvel for the church service, did he go outside the familiar compass of his own boundlessly free world.

" I expect many of you wonder why anybody should live away up on the edge of the moors," Fleming has said, " well, when I was a boy the difference was even greater than it is now. There were no cars, but we still had our feet. As boys we had many advantages over the boys living in the towns. We automatically learned many things that they missed, and it was just the chance of living away from people which taught us those things."

At ten, however, Loudoun Moor School could keep him no longer ; the time had come for him to join his brothers, John and Robert, at Darvel School. So now he began to walk four miles downhill into Darvel at eight o'clock each morning and four miles uphill to Lochfield each afternoon at the close of the school day, in spring and autumn through the equinoctial gales, in winter through the crunching frosts and soft snows. Often he was soaked to the skin, but revelling in the life out of doors, he felt it as a passing inconvenience and suffered no harm, and the blood coursed invigoratingly through his veins as he dried himself before a glowing peat fire.

" Certainly," he himself observes, " the four miles down in the morning and the four miles up at night took time and energy, but it did a lot of good and it was not wasted time because we learned things. You might go up the Glen, you might take a short cut across the fields and you picked up many interesting things about wild Nature that you might not have learned at school. If I had got home five minutes after leaving school, what would I have done that would have been useful?"

Mr. Gorrie, the headmaster of Darvel School, "one of Nature's gentlemen if ever there was one," guided his boys through a curriculum that included Latin. He was a small, spare man and very alert, and the easier informalities of Loudoun Moor School were replaced by his severer approach. Although Mr. Gorrie made his presence felt throughout the school, Fleming for the most part was instructed by his own master, a Mr. Peter Craig. He continued to find that school work came easily to him and he was still able to please his teachers without any excessive diligence on his part.

Although he and his brothers were now thrown among town boys, they could not help feeling that they had it over their companions in certain respects which to them remained important. "Living as we did at the end of the road and up on the edge of the moor," he says, "we considered ourselves a bit better than the boys in the town, because when they came up they did not know how to climb, they did not know how to guddle trout in the burn, and they did not know where to find peewits eggs." Denied the interests of the countryside to which they had been accustomed even during the break for meals, they often spent their dinner hour watching the navvies building the railway between Darvel and Newmilns.

It was in the Glen Water that he guddled for trout, those speckled torpedoes which launched themselves towards dark refuges beneath rocks the moment his shadow fell across the stream. Elusive creatures, they challenged his ingenuity, which he exercised in devising ways and means of catching them. Sweet and tasty, their frequent appearance on the breakfast-table was his reward, and the tangible evidence of his skill. And how to catch rabbits, nervous and jumpy, taking so quickly to their holes? They too challenged his ingenuity, his fertile mind set his strong hands and deft fingers to work producing a variety of methods for ensnaring the young and tender ones for the pot. "He was always thinking something up," relates his brother, Robert, "but if it didn't work, he lost no time in modifying it or discarding it altogether and thinking up something else."

With Robert for company he watched the homing birds coming down to earth, and his keen vision unerringly marked their landing places, so that he would know precisely where to find their nests. "My powers of observation," he has said, "were sharpened by my search for peewits eggs in the fields and moors, my patience increased by the guddling for the trout in the Glen Water."

By the time he was twelve, Alexander Fleming possessed a sturdy frame, his legs, indefatigable, could carry him mile after mile, the glow in his cheeks advertised the foundations of excellent health, reserves of vigour and inexhaustible stamina. Now he performed some of the many tasks that fell due at Lochfield each day. He helped to cut the peats, to load them into the waggons and take them for stacking and storing, ready for use as winter fuel. In the summer, while others were hay-making, Robert and he scoured the moors, a collie at their heels, keeping an eye on the sheep or tracking down any that had strayed.

At twelve, however, he had reached the age limit prescribed for the pupils of Darvel School, and it was decided that he should continue his education at the Kilmarnock Academy, a big day school. As a Provost of Darvel has put it: "Fortunately for us and for the world, when the time came to decide whether this boy should go back to the land or stay at school, the decision was that he should carry on with his studies." Kilmarnock was some sixteen miles away and the daily journey to and fro was out of the question because there was no convenient form of transport available. He was therefore to board out, attend school and return to Lochfield at week-ends. It meant he had to stride home from Newmilns station each Friday evening during term-time, a distance of over six miles. And this march had to be repeated at cockcrow on Monday mornings in the opposite direction, through the darkness in winter, through the rolling white mists blowing down from the hills, and as days lengthened, through the violet shadows turning into crimson dawns. Yet the prospect left him undaunted ; he had ranged the moorlands so far and so wide that he knew them intimately.

Of this phase of his life he remarks : " The railway wasn't

finished yet so every Friday night I had to walk from Newmilns station to Lochfield, except sometimes when I took the old horse bus to Darvel. But it would be regarded as a crime now to allow a schoolboy to walk six miles from Newmilns to Lochfield ; it would not be allowed that he should walk the four miles from Lochfield to Darvel. Well, it certainly kept me fit anyway."

Kilmarnock rejoices in its connections with both Robert Louis Stevenson and Robert Burns ; indeed, the anxious hands of posterity have collected the original manuscripts of Burns and placed them in the Kilmarnock museum. But Alexander Fleming's memories of that town are not of its historical associations but of " a very big school on the top of a hill, a very good school then," where a system of constant examinations kept the boys always at it, and which he believes provided him with excellent lessons in how to be a good examinee. After about eighteen months there, other plans were forming. He left Kilmarnock Academy with the lineaments of character and personality growing more strongly defined. Moreover, his own instinctive gifts of observation, trained by constant attention to the processes of Nature, were beginning to combine with a developing reason.

CHAPTER III

THE CLASSROOM, THE CITY, ST. MARY'S

" THE STORY of Penicillin," Fleming once said, " has a certain romance in it and helps to illustrate the amount of chance, or fortune, or fate, or destiny, call it what you like, in anybody's career. I might have stayed on the land and become a farmer—not at Lochfield, for my brother Hugh was there—but on some other farm in the neighbourhood. I might have been a very good farmer, who knows, and I might have had the finest Ayrshire herd in the country. However, I was sent to London to my brother Thomas there. . . ."

This change from Scotland to London was, according to him, the first of several such strokes of fortune which profoundly influenced his life. But if they appeared to be disjointed and unconnected at the time of their occurrence, they form in retrospect a perfectly coherent sequence of events like a pre-ordained design leading to a great scientific discovery.

Thomas Fleming had studied medicine at Glasgow University, and after some general practice in the North, had come to London and set up as an oculist in the Marylebone Road, where he had quickly been successful. The two young Flemings, John and Robert, had already come south to join him, and it was now Alexander's turn. He arrived in London in 1895, when he was fourteen years old, and London became the city of his adoption. Yet he was never to lose his Scottish identity, always retained the soft accents of his native country, chose many of his friends among Scottish people and joined the London Scottish Volunteers.

This abiding sense of fidelity to his origins was well illustrated in a letter written by him on April 26th, 1951, to Robin Bailes, an old regimental friend. " I came back a few days ago from Pakistan, where I was for ten days. There were two incidents there which might interest you. I landed at Karachi and after some days I flew to Peshawar and drove up the

Kyber Pass to the borders of Afghanistan. Then I flew back to Lahore for two days. When I got to the airport to return to Karachi, I found the Pipe Band of the Pakistan Army Medical Corps. I enclose the programme, which is interesting, as my chief qualification for such a reception was that I had once been a private in the London Scottish. They marched up and down in great style, and their piping would have been no disgrace to the Scottish. They finished with Auld Lang Syne as I boarded the plane.

" The same night I had dinner with the Old Comrades in Karachi. We had a very good evening in Mackay's house. This was the bright spot of my journey and I am grateful to the Old Comrades ".

This " clannishness " as the English see it, the ineradicable feeling of "my ain folk", again comes out in an observation he made about a trip to Brazil in 1946. " I was in Brazil, in Rio de Janeiro. One night the telephone rang and I heard a voice with a homely accent. It was Mrs. Cairns, who was Mary Morton of Darvel, and she had been in Rio fifteen years. She still had a wonderful Darvel accent, and it was a pleasure to hear it after listening to Portugese for a week."

For the fourteen-year-old Alexander Fleming, now journeying southwards to London, it was farewell to his own windswept moorlands, to the Glen Water and the guddling for trout, to the search for peewit's eggs. It was farewell to Lochfield. Instead of the heather in season, the soft grass underfoot, the exhilarations of infinite spaces, it was now the eternal tread on hard city pavements, the urban life with its sense of confinement. In London he was at the crowded centre of bewildering contradictions, where the depressing poverty of tenements contrasted with sumptuous doings in great town houses ; he was in the closest proximity to the tumultuous repercussions of the distant South African War, to the closing scenes of Queen Victoria's long reign as they were for ever being committed to history, and afterwards to the opening scenes of our own disturbed epoch with its ever-hastening mutation of society, of manners, modes and morals.

Once in London he resumed his schooling at the Polytechnic in Regent Street, where his brother Robert was studying.

27

His new life was not without its compensations, for there were the novelties of the London scene to excite his young mind, and he was still among members of his family. Especially he had the company of Robert with whom he had roamed and climbed in Scotland and to whom he felt very close. Of the education he received he trenchantly comments : " For a short time I went to the Regent Street Polytechnic and I found that the work which the boys were doing was just what I had done two years before."

In 1897, Thomas Fleming moved to another house—in York Street, Baker Street, and the brothers were then joined by one or other of their sisters in turn, who supervised their domestic arrangements. In the same year, at the age of sixteen, Alexander Fleming left the Polytechnic and began work in the offices of a shipping company in Leadenhall Street. " It was forced on me by economic reasons," he says. Even this inconspicuous period of his life did not escape subsequent romanticization. According to one journal he was employed by an American concern owning the fastest ships plying between New York and Southampton, until the firm's fleet was commandeered for use as auxiliary cruisers at the outbreak of the Spanish-American War, forcing him to consider the selection of a different career. Chronological confusion disposes of the legend without trouble : the Spanish-American War took place between April and August of 1898, and he did not begin his medical career until 1901, for quite other reasons as he himself bears out.

By then his brother, Thomas, had decided to practice in Harley Street, and so Alexander, with others of the family, moved to a house in Ealing where, to their pleasure, they were joined by their mother who came from Scotland to take over from their sister, Mary, the responsibilities of the household. The sisters in turn married : Jean a Darvel doctor, Mary a veterinary surgeon, and Grace a business man.

Meanwhile, his brothers, John and Robert, were busy getting through the Ophthalmic Opticians' examinations of the Worshipful Company of Spectaclers, before starting a business of their own, which, from modest beginnings, they built into one of the leading Optical Works Laboratories in the country. To-day John is no more, but Robert remains to direct its activities with the assistance of newer generations of Flemings.

Alexander became acquainted with the operations of shipping companies, and with the fascinating by-ways of the City of London in the environs of Leadenhall Street, of Lloyds and of the Baltic Exchange, but his wage packet remained as unexciting as his prospects. Yet there was a stoicism in his character which enabled him to apply himself to his unvarying duties and to perform them to the satisfaction of his superiors.

Towards the end of 1900, he and his brothers, John and Robert, joined the London Scottish Volunteers. An entry in the records of the regiment shows that his number was 6392, and that he belonged to H Coy. "As regards H Coy." he observed in later years, "nobody in other Companies had ever heard of it ; it was stuck at the end of a column of a thousand men, it never heard the pipes and could only keep in step by sheer will-power. Naturally the men of H Coy. were self-willed, self-centred and a law unto themselves ; but remember the surprises of the battalion when one year, despite the crack shots in other Companies, H won the Celestial (shooting trophy)." Fleming himself contributed to that victory for he was an exceedingly good shot and represented the Scottish in team shoots at Bisley, where he won several prizes. "But," he complains good-naturedly, "I was never even offered a stripe and got no further in the regiment than being a Pioneer, and for a short time a Scout."

The unlooked-for advantages of lowly rank were only made plain to him in August, 1945, during a voyage to America on the old *Aquitania*, when he noted the Hodden Grey kilt worn by O.C. Troops on board. This turned out to be Colonel Lyall Grant who promptly asked him to tell the men in non-technical terms how he discovered penicillin. It was a gloriously sunny day yet the ship's lounge was crammed full. Then Colonel Lyall Grant explained : "Some thirty years ago, Sir Alexander and I served in the same regiment. He was a humble private, whereas I was a noble piper in the band. Perhaps it was a feeling of frustration at not being able to play the pipes that drove him to do the next best thing and discover penicillin ! "

His association with the Scottish was a happy one ; it gave him the opportunity of indulging a passion for the open air and for sport that had been bred in him during early boyhood. More, it took him into a community of men, like him exiled from the land of their birth for a variety of reasons, yet bound together by the similarity of their origins and their sentiments.

And now once again in swift succession come more of those decisive interventions of chance to which he refers. He had earned a place in the regimental swimming and water polo team, and one day he took part in a contest with St. Mary's Hospital. This ordinary event in due time assumed a far from ordinary significance, for, in his own words : " Something happened over which I had no control which made it possible for me to become a medical student." In 1901 he received his share of a small legacy, and this enabled him to consider some alternative to a career in a shipping office. " My brother, Thomas," he continues, " pushed me into medicine. Then I had to choose a medical school. There are twelve such schools in London. I did not know any of them, but I had played water-polo against St. Mary's, so to St. Mary's I went. The choice of a school for this very insufficient reason had a great influence on my career, for at the time I joined St. Mary's as a student, Almroth Wright joined as a teacher in bacteriology."

Surely no sporting encounter between two teams has ever provided an example so curious of the incalculable manifestations of destiny ! A water-polo player in a regimental side afterwards decides he wishes to be a doctor and enters the hospital he knows only through its prowess at a game. He then feels the influence of a man of genius and, without any hesitation, follows in his footsteps as a bacteriologist. During the course of the years, by some perverse magic, a substance of incredible healing power is laid casually before his eyes. By the greatest good fortune his are trained and observant eyes ; he does not " with appropriate language " throw away a contaminated Petri dish. " I'm just a canny Scot who never throws anything away," he jokes in telling the story, but such is the unexpectedness of great things, and the bizarre offerings of destiny frequently represent the prelude to matters of overbearing importance in human affairs.

It was, however, not enough for his brother to "push" him into medicine; first he had to matriculate and next to sit for a hospital examination. He easily won the Senior Entrance Scholarship in Natural Science and so began his career as a medical student. Dr. David Carmalt Jones who was at St. Mary's during Fleming's student days and who, like him, worked with Wright, gives a vivid and entertaining account of the hospital and the medical school at that period. He says:

"The hospital itself was a gloomy place, and if a cross-draught is important, the old wards were not well designed, though the patients seemed to do all right in them. They were quite without aesthetic attractions. The School was worse, shabby, squalid rooms, ill-lighted and coarsely furnished. But the hospital routine for students and residents was good. Clinical work for students generally began after their Anatomy and Physiology. They gained their first experiences in the Casualty Ward, opening abscesses, passing catheters, dressing and bandaging wounds. They were also taught (and well taught) how to extract teeth. No local anaesthetic was available for the single extraction; the patient sat on an ordinary wooden chair and hung on and hoped. And bore up.

"We must have done some dreadful things, but we did begin to handle patients. We got surprisingly little teaching, but clinical medicine is a thing which cannot be taught but must be learned. What little we knew we found out for ourselves with such help as our house physicians could give us. They were, so to speak, only a page ahead of us, and we could go to them and admit: 'I can't hear this murmur you say is there'. They would then show us where to listen and try to imitate the sound.

"A skiagram (X-ray picture) of the chest gives a far more accurate indication of its contents, but in the view of my generation, it should only be used to confirm diagnosis.

"At the beginning of the century, medicine was in quilibrium and had not yet begun to slant over positively towards the scientific side.

"I do not think the clinical teaching was particularly good; the lectures in systematic medicine were poor.

"I was 'on the district' for a month, getting my experience in midwifery. The patient's husband called at the hospital; at night he was sent on to your digs and he conducted you to the case in the back streets off the Edgware Road beyond the

Metropolitan Music Hall, or in the back streets off the Harrow Road and further out. Many of these places were pretty bad. Often enough there was only one room, though I never saw more than one family in it. The working man had two problems in life : to make a pound a week and then to live on it. There were labourers, horsekeepers, carters and unskilled workers. Fortunately ninety-nine cases of confinement only want leaving alone. Or so we believed."

Of Fleming, the student, two of his old colleagues offer enlightening views. Professor Charles Pannett, who was with him at medical school from 1902 says : " His instinctive sense of observation was most acute even in those days. I felt he could gauge the slant of examiners' minds in some astonishing way, even to the point of anticipating just the sort of questions they were going to ask him ! " Dr. Leonard Colebrook, a co-worker in Wright's laboratory, who shared rooms with him for a period remarks : " I don't think I ever saw him burn the midnight oil or sit glued endlessly to his books. He certainly didn't give me the impression of putting himself out unduly. I believe he had a formidable memory." He seems to have changed little since the days in the " wee country school " where his brother, Robert, noticed that he had never needed to apply himself to his lessons with excessive diligence. At any rate studies did not keep him from participating in ordinary student activities ; he was regularly in the hospital shooting team, he played water-polo, swam and took part in amateur theatricals. Indeed, to this day there hangs a photograph on his laboratory wall showing himself and Lord Moran filling women's parts in a hospital production.

Whether selected for him by some wayward concatenation of events as he maintains, or by some deeper intuition within himself, he had lighted upon a vocation perfectly suited to him. The scholarship he had obtained in 1901 was only a beginning. Year after year the records of the medical school showed his name at the top of the examination lists, and as a laconic entry in a directory now has it : *Won almost all class prizes and scholarships, honours in Physiology, Pharmacology, Medicine, Pathology, Forensic Medicine and Hygiene.*

CHAPTER IV

THE CHALLENGE OF MEDICAL RESEARCH

SPEAKING of his days at medical school Fleming has said : " The first event of importance was the coming of Almroth Wright to St. Mary's Hospital when I was a student. He was just beginning vaccine therapy and the opsonic index had appeared shortly before I qualified."

When Wright accepted the Chair of Pathology in 1902, his department (then too grand a word for it perhaps) consisted of a basement in which the microscopes quaked at the passing of every underground train. He soon changed that, however, gathering together some helpers and moving to steadier and more presentable quarters on the second floor, equipped with tiled benches and glass slabs. He was already a renowned figure, for before his arrival at St. Mary's he had successfully begun preventive inoculation against typhoid using heat-killed cultures. It was a momentous contribution towards the salvation of medicine from what he had himself described as its bankruptcy, and in its achievement he had borne scientific technique far forward.

Now, in an era when immunology was the main preoccupation of bacteriologists, he became the exponent of a theme which rang new in medical science, and which he had for the most part evolved out of Metchnikov's observations of phagocytosis.

To Metchnikov, who belonged to the Pasteur Institute in Paris, and to his disciples, the cause of immunity from disease was the white corpuscle in the blood, the phagocyte, a living cell that engulfed and digested the attacking microbe. This was phagocytosis. To the Germans, Koch, von Behring, Pfeiffer and others, the cause of immunity was the bactericidal power of the blood-fluid. The ensuing controversy between the French and the German schools has been called the " New

Thirty Years War ", waged by Metchnikov and his partisans with courage and varying fortune against the blood-fluid theory so tenaciously defended by the most eminent biologists and bacteriologists in German science.

Wright was familiar with these arguments blowing about the Continent but, mindful of Pasteur's work on anthrax, chicken cholera and rabies, of his own endeavours with anti-typhoid immunization and the demonstration of specific antibodies after inoculation, his questing mind settled upon the idea that there existed in the human and the animal tremendous latent forces ready to be evoked by appropriate stimuli. He therefore set before himself certain pro-positions :

> Prevention of widespread disease was not always possible, but what about their cure ? Had not Pasteur successfully inoculated patients against rabies *after* they had been bitten by mad dogs, when they were already incubating the disease ?
> Could not patients incubating other microbic infections already manifest by some localized focus of disease, such as a boil, be treated by inoculation ?
> Were the phagocytes of a person with a boil more or less active than those of a healthy person ?
> Could phagocytes be activated by inoculation of a vaccine ?
> How long would the effects of such an inoculation last ?
> There seemed to be no change in the blood of a person with a boil, so the process of recovery from such a condition probably differed from the process of recovery in cases of typhoid.
> The answer to these questions might well be available in Metchnikov's observations of phagocytosis. There were thirty-five thousand million of these wandering cells in the normal adult's blood stream, capable of devouring microbes. In addition there were prodigious numbers in the bone marrow and fixed tissues. The body's immunity or resistance to a particular microbe, in all its variations, probably depended upon phagocytosis.

He then commenced a careful enquiry into the subject of the phagocytes and their behaviour. The information at his disposal was sporadic and often equivocal, but he and his assistant, Dr. S. R. Douglas, found that phagocytosis was more complex than Metchnikov believed. It was not enough for phagocytes and microbes to come together, the microbes had in some fashion to be "prepared" before the phagocytes could swallow and digest them. They concluded that this was brought about by some property in the blood-serum which they named opsonin, a derivation from the Greek word *opsono* : *I prepare victuals for.*

"It was a fundamental discovery of the first importance," states Dr. Leonard Colebrook, Wright's biographer, "possibly the most far-reaching since Pasteur discovered that fermentation was due to bacterial action". Apart from synthesizing the opposing views of the French and German schools, it clarified ideas about the mechanism of recovery from microbic disease, provided a new and precise method of diagnosis of at least some microbic diseases and opened a wide field for exploration in their treatment.

Moreover, the measurement of man's opsonic power would make possible the development of vaccine therapy against these diseases. If by an appropriate dose of vaccine the opsonic power could be restored to normal, then the phagocytes should be able to deal with the invading microbes.

And it was possible to establish a patient's opsonic power or opsonic index by testing a blood-sample under the microscope. The serum of all healthy people will allow approximately the same number of bacteria to be ingested by each phagocyte, but the serum of the person infected by a particular organism will allow the ingestion of many more or many less. There is thus a divergence from the normal. If the serum allows of less than normal ingestion, that is, if the opsonic index is low, the correct treatment is to inject a vaccine of the infecting organisms, killed by heat, into some healthy part of the body. When all goes well, the tissues make antibodies which pass into the blood-stream and help to destroy the bacteria in the infected site.

"This," says Dr. Colebrook, "was the basic idea behind the growing point of medicine for twenty years".

Hitherto diagnosis had depended almost wholly on an interpretation of physical symptoms ; the way to discover anything about the heart or the stomach or the lungs was by palpation, by percussion, or by auscultation. A famous physician, the story goes, having listened to a patient's chest, proclaimed with the utmost gravity : " Sounds to me like the influenza bacillus ". Surgeons, flaunting the delicacy of their touch, the sensitivity of their fingers, lost much of their conceit when challenged to locate by feel a half-crown piece concealed beneath several folds of a blanket. They seldom succeeded.

Across this " nakedness of the land in medicine " Wright's voice had resounded. In an article which he headed " The World's Greatest Problem ", he embodied for the public the burden of the challenge he had often thrown down to his students and others ; it made its vigorous impact on Fleming.

> " Of all the evils which befall man in his civilized state, the evil of disease is incomparably the greatest. In comparison with the chance of winning control over this evil, every other thing ought to be counted as a loss. If the belief is nurtured that the medical art of to-day can effectually intervene in the course of disease, this ought to be dismissed as an illusion. . . .
> " The scientific knowledge which alone can avail in the conflict with disease is—practically all of it—still to seek."

Now, however, the bacteriologist could offer instead of the older diagnostic uncertainties an exactitude resting upon what he saw under the lens of his microscope. He could measure bactericidal antibodies, make a count of microbes in a culture, observe the intriguing doings of phagocytes and of those countless germs mortally hostile to the human organism, which multiplied with such incredible profligacy. Was not Wright prophesying that in vaccine therapy there existed a general therapeutic method which would be applicable to the treatment of all kinds of localized bacterial infections ? Was he not on the way towards coining his electrifying aphorism that " the physician of the future will be an immunizer " ?

Even George Bernard Shaw, who knew Wright, was shown the opsonic technique. " I smell drama ! " he exclaimed one day during a visit to the laboratory upon being told that the time was coming when a doctor would have to determine whether a man's life was worth saving or not. He made a drama of it in " The Doctor's Dilemma ", and during the course of the play makes Ridgeon (supposedly a caricature of Wright) explain :

" The phagocytes won't eat the microbes unless the microbes are nicely buttered for them. Well, the patient manufactures the butter for himself all right ; but my discovery is that the manufacture of that butter, which I call opsonin, goes on in the system by ups and downs—Nature being always rhythmical, you know—and that what the inoculation does is to stimulate the ups and downs, as the case may be. I call the up-grade the positive phase and the down-grade the negative phase. Everything depends on your inoculating at the right moment. Inoculate when the patient is in the negative phase and you kill ; inoculate when the patient is in the positive phase and you cure. . . .

" Send a drop of the patient's blood to the laboratory at St. Anne's ; and in fifteen minutes I'll give you his opsonin index figures. If the figure is one, inoculate and cure ; if it's under point eight, inoculate and kill. That's my discovery. . . "

It was thus in a tonic mental climate, charged with expectations and excitements that Fleming approached the end of his distinguished career as a medical student. At long last, it seemed, a solution to the problem of bacterial diseases was in sight. All that remained was to find the proper dose of vaccine for administration in any particular infection, and cure was nearer. There were scoffers, of course, who spoke derisively of " so many lab-tricks ", but the spectacle of organized combat against those unseen enemies of the human organism swarming a " world of the infinitely small " was enthralling, and many felt themselves poised on the threshold of an Augustan Age in medicine.

Now Wright's theory in all its ramifications awaited substantiation in the laboratory, awaited the proofs of efficacy in its clinical application. There had to be experiment, experiment, and more experiment, and more hands to conduct them. But there was a dearth of research workers, and Wright declared : " We are not, in fact, making any effort worthy of the name to solve the problems of disease, and we have not in England any appreciable number of workers engaged on the task of medical research. This is due to economical reasons. A young man who proposes to take up medical research as his life work finds himself immediately confronted in his own person with those very fundamental and primitive problems of obtaining subsistence, and clothes, and a shelter over his head."

The material outlook seemed bleak, but Fleming's tastes

were frugal, his wants simple, and he was not dismayed by the promise of only small comforts. The alternatives were plain : the ampler prospects of the practitioner's days or the quest "beyond the ranges" of which Wright had spoken. The field of medical research, almost bare, almost unploughed, had yielded a crop meagre in quantity but of great preciousness. Another hand to the plough, unturned soil turned over and who knew, it might yield fresh crops even more precious.

Fleming's choice was never in doubt. "On the day after I qualified in medicine," he says, "I joined Wright's laboratory. I have been there ever since."

That choice was testimony of a perspicacious and intuitive mind, warmed by the glow of a revolutionary idea, possessing the vision to sense the patterns of a far-reaching metamorphosis taking place in medicine. "Most scientists," he asserts, "are artists in a sense. Unless they have vision they can do comparatively little with their formulae." Nor did he see research as a gamble. "When you gamble," he has declared, "you may eventually go broke, but with research you may make a failure, then another failure, then others, but you never go broke." A thousand lost experiments perhaps, bafflement and chagrin, with only the hope of discovery fluttering before the imagination and beckoning further along the road. Courage and spirit were necessary to face the incorrigible caprices of Nature.

It was certainly not ambition that drove him to research. "Ambitions have a way of growing," he has warned, "one success breeding the desire for another. That's all right so long as personal success is not obtained at the expense of our fellow creatures. Happily in medicine success cannot come that way, but there are degrees of success. Many a country doctor has had more real success than the most famous leaders of the profession in any big city. He has by his kindness gentleness and sympathy endeared himself to his community, and after all, that's what counts, not the accumulation of wealth or the adulation of sycophants."

There were also the biddings of other voices ; the echo of Wright's moving phrase, "a pain in the mind" ; the undertones of idealism ; the cry to conscience of humanity in its predicament, so admirably evoked by Bertrand Russell in his " Free Man's Worship " :

" The life of Man is a long march through the night, surrounded by invisible foes, tortured by weariness and pain towards a goal that few can hope to reach, and where none may tarry long. One by one, as they march, our comrades vanish from our sight, seized by the orders of omnipotent death. Very brief is the time in which we can help them, in which their misery or happiness is decided."

Dr. Serge Metalnikov of the Pasteur Institute in Paris has also described the extent of the human predicament and the call to fight against it :

" The instinct of self-preservation pushes us to fight against death, to avoid unfavourable circumstances, to adapt ourselves and to defend our bodies from innumerable enemies within and without. Life is really a struggle against death. Men are put to death by parasites and by the blind forces of nature : that is the inevitable and universal fact. Can we reconcile ourselves to this truth which makes life absurd and wretched ? "

Asked to explain his presence in medical research, Fleming will shrug his shoulders and give the most matter-of-fact of reasons. " I just drifted into it," he once said, but mostly he is inclined to attribute it to the workings of chance. His reticence discourages the postulation of any enticing metaphysical hypotheses, but a life-time's devotion to research is in itself the whole, satisfying and self-evident answer to questions of this sort.

Not only did Wright draw attention to the difficult circumstances for research workers, he demanded of those who wished to join him exacting standards and renovated attitudes of mind. "Reason," he insisted, " must take a dominant place in our work," and in his "Principles of Microscopy" he stated :

" Everyone who has to use a microscope must decide for himself the question as to whether he will do so in accordance with a system of rule-of-thumb, or whether he will seek to supersede this by a system of reasoned action, based upon a scientific study of his instrument, and a consideration of the scientific principles of microscopical technique. The present text-book has no message for those who are content to follow a system of rule-of-thumb, it addresses itself to those who are dissatisfied with the results thus obtained, and who desire to master the scientific principles of microscopy even at the cost of some intellectual effort."

Bacteriology was swiftly emerging from a rudimentary state when even a smoothly-operating syringe did not exist, and when the extraction of a blood-sample from the vein was nearly unheard of. In the new medicine, measurement and experiment played a growing part, calling for new apparatus and new techniques at every stage in order to advance. His assistants were expected to fabricate their own devices, to be able to call upon their own creative flair and their own powers of invention. As the German physiologist, Ludwig, maintained: " The whole of science lies in technique."

To this demand Fleming was to respond with extraordinary aptitude. Endowed with " wonderful hands " and a highly ingenious turn of mind, he was to make himself into a superb technician. " A great bacteriologist ? " a former colleague of his once exclaimed, " posterity will decide that, but I can tell you he is a great technician, a great craftsman."

Finally, Wright expected that they should always keep in contact with the sick, and as for hours of work, it was certain only that they would be excessively long, excessively strenuous and more than ought to be asked of average humans. But theirs, on the other hand, was no average enterprise.

On August 6th, 1906, which was his twenty-fifth birthday, and the day after he had qualified in medicine, Fleming joined Wright.

CHAPTER V

THE FLEDGLING BACTERIOLOGIST

WHEN FLEMING commenced his career as a bacteriologist, Wright's Inoculation Department at St. Mary's Hospital, whose origins reposed in a ramshackle basement, consisted of two laboratories with preparation rooms in the east half of the Clarence Wing on the second floor, and several other smaller rooms. To some it was an inner sanctum of mumbo-jumbo, packed with the arcana of a suspect and cranky wizard ; to others it was a shrine, inhabited by a high priest and his initiates who were custodians of a supreme mystery, and who, by means not too well appreciated, had gained possession of the keys to a medical millenium.

The truth of the matter was, of course, far removed from any odours of the miraculous ; it was simply that a new class of scientist-technicians under inspiriting leadership were breaking into uncharted terrain and taking soundings in unnavigated waters ; these competent and vigorous young men were slowly tilting the balance of the structure of medicine in their favour, and the mould of " doctoring in the 'Nineties " was cracking. They had few predecents to which they could conveniently resort, they were the architects of their own scientific tradition, the pioneers of their own techniques. They had a working hypothesis to guide them in their labours, and as they reached out for inviolable experimental data and subjected their deductions to scrupulous analysis, they were in no small measure endeavouring to show that what they had apprehended by the exercise of imagination and intuition was demonstrable in the laboratory. The wings of quest hovered continually above them ; has not Fleming himself pointed out that " most scientists are artists in a sense ? Unless they have vision," he said, "they can do comparatively little with their formulae." They required more than a mere agglomeration of facts inferred from the routines of experiment to build their edifice ; they required to employ the widest range of their faculties which, in coalescing, touched off the springs of discovery.

Their working hypothesis rested upon the earlier investigations of Wright and his helpers leading to the introduction of anti-typhoid vaccines and afterwards to the exposition of the opsonic index and the practice of vaccine therapy. The bodies of men and animals could produce specific antibodies to harmful microbes, and those antibodies operated exclusively against the agent which had provoked their existence. It is to this day a little-understood manifestation whose occurrence cannot quite be explained, yet it remains that the serum of an animal inoculated with the cholera microbe, for example, becomes destructive to that microbe alone and to no other.

Moreover, Wright had perceived that typhoid fever was not merely an infection of the bowel ; it proved mortal when the microbe broke out into the blood-stream and generalized itself. The blood had to be made lethal to the microbe and it could then be contained. To achieve this he utilized a safe, heat-killed culture, which nevertheless retained its immunizing powers, and it was shown that specific antibodies were created after inoculation. Scientific immunization was in this way carried beyond the illustrious beginnings made by Pasteur. Now the cultures had to be standardized, the number of microbes in a culture had to be counted, the antibodies produced in the blood of persons inoculated with different doses of culture had to be measured, the duration of persistence of such antibodies had to be established.

Hitherto nobody had attempted to measure bactericidal antibodies or to count the microbes in a culture ; to do so clamoured for technical innovations, for the elaboration of a completely new order in laboratory methods and techniques. " The whole *raison d'être* of a new technique " declared Wright, " is to eke out the inadequate skill of our hands by the contributory work of our brains." His biographer, Colebrook, says : " The development of vaccine therapy, which pivoted on the quantitative study of phagosytosis, called for yet another series of technical procedures. All these new procedures had become quite a considerable battery of weapons for use in medical research, and Wright felt they ought to be embodied in a handbook for the wider use of workers all over the world. He accordingly set about the task of describing in full detail the simpler processes of glass-blowing, the calibration and use of capillary pipettes, and the many methods of blood examination which he and his colleagues had worked out. It made a book of unique character and was called 'The Technique of the Teat and the Capillary Glass Tube.'"

In this technical sphere Fleming displayed a very special flair, struck his *metier*, and equipped himself for some of the brilliant work he was to do in connection with antiseptics during the First World War. Speaking of their association with Wright during this period Colebrook remarks : " He received invaluable help from Alexander Fleming." In later years Fleming was generously to say that anything he accomplished in his life was due to his work with Wright, whose unending inventiveness had stimulated his own and other men's skill, yet he too had an uncanny eye for the practical. An old colleague of his tells that sometimes when Wright permitted himself to be carried away by the force of his own eloquence in outlining some procedure, it was Fleming who listened with detachment and who said quietly : " It won't work, chief." Sometimes Wright launched into his disquisition for a second time with redoubled eloquence, no doubt in the hope of carrying his point. But still Fleming would listen without interruption till he had finished and repeat simply : " It won't work, chief." More often than not it didn't.

The consolations of medical research, however, lie not only in the pursuit of recondite enquiry but in the application of its proven conclusions to the relief of stricken men and women. Since Wright insisted that his workers should keep contact with the sick, the corridors leading to their laboratory were besieged by patients. Fleming and his colleagues were thus provided with ample clinical material, and he had the opportunity of meeting almost every disease thought to be caused by microbes, and of diagnosing bacteriologically a host of complaints. The out-patients attended in the afternoons, in always increasing numbers, some of them given up as hopeless by doctors who had exhausted more orthodox physicks. The scene oddly recalls Duclaux' account of Pasteur's own laboratory : " Many have described the strange spectacle offered by the laboratory and the courtyard near to it, where assembled a picturesque and polyglot crowd of bitten individuals come to beg of science the end of their apprehensions and the certainty of to-morrow. But what has not been mentioned enough is the contagious confidence which spread through all the newcomers—and made of them believers— whose faith contributed to their recovery."

From each of the patients who came to Wright's department for help, a drop of blood had to be taken, put into a container and labelled. Sometimes they received an inoculation immediately, sometimes on the day following, after the result of the blood-test became known. Slides were then prepared for microscopic examination, a task generally occupying an hour or two. After dinner the staff returned and the work began in earnest. Dozens of blood-samples, laid out on white tiles, were scrutinized in turn ; pipettes were made and researchers, pricking themselves, drew their own blood to serve as normal controls. " We were the human pin-cushions, we stuck things into ourselves so often," remarks Dr. Colebrook.

In that laboratory one of the workers, Dr. Wells, while investigating an unusual infection, caught it, and eighteen months later, died ; Dr. Leonard Noon, another worker, contracted pulmonary tuberculosis and later he, too, died. Fleming himself describes one of the occasions on which he played his own guinea pig. " On Saturday," he writes, " I had inoculated into my median basilic vein one hundred and fifty million staphylococcus vaccine. On Sunday I felt generally ill, with nausea, headache, etc. Temperature on Sunday evening reached 101°." Happily he also records that " everything cleared up by Monday evening."

The last and most arduous among the jobs of the day arrived when the opsonic tests were set up and the counts made. If things went wrong—and they frequently did in those early days—the whole collection was jettisoned, and back to the beginning to repeat the process all over again. Not a single soul dreamed of leaving until all the work was completed, no matter what the hour. " When I entered the bacteriological laboratory at St. Mary's Hospital on my birthday, August 6th, 1906," says Fleming, "marked in the laboratory log-book is, 'Enter Fleming, exit sixteen hours daily.' 'Enter Fleming' was true, but 'exit sixteen hours daily' was false, for we worked all that for years afterwards." Talking of those times, his friend, Professor Pannett, relates : " Fleming has great strength and an amazing capacity for working until all hours and appearing the next morning before everybody else, fresh and punctual. His physical resources, founded upon his love of an open-air life, have been always a tremendous asset to him."

Many of the sick crowding the department and awaiting treatment with endless patience, with resignation lit by the gleams of hope, responded to vaccine therapy, especially those with localized infections. Fleming and his fellow-workers watched the slow process of cure, occasionally broken by the exciting and the dramatic. Indolent ulcers healed, tuberculous glands disappeared ; boils, carbuncles and streptococcal conditions were resolved in due time. A woman with lupus : cured. A penniless American seaman who had struggled up to London from Plymouth with a swollen ankle that was tuberculous : cured. A fisherman's boy from Land's End with tuberculosis of the spine : cured. A derelict potman with immense tuberculous ulcers of the neck : cured. Only he had nowhere to go when he got better so he remained to work for years as a factotum in the very laboratories in which they had made a new man of him. He always carried on his person the chit given to him by Dr. Carmalt Jones asking that Wright's department should deal with his case. Sometime he produced it, and with a proud, cheerful grin remarked : " This was my life-saver and no mistake." On the whole, their successes with invasive infections, that is, septicaemic infections, were modest.

" My department " said Wright, " is a republic as all the world ought to be." In reality it was a benevolent despotism, even though he was never heard to give an order. A big-boned man with an impressive presence, he was always ready to devote his whole attention to any task upon which his young colleagues might be engaged. He never praised lavishly, and was once heard quoting " Falstaff " at an unfortunate : " Well, if I be served such another trick, I'll have my brains ta'en out and buttered and give them to a dog for a New Year's gift."

In that department Fleming witnessed many memorable scenes. They took place round about midnight, after the tea had been brewed and discussions had sprung up during a respite. There was argument, debate, disagreement, shop ; there was always somebody standing by to throw in a Rabelaisian tale. It was a cosmopolitan gathering, consisting of men from America, Canada, India, Norway, Denmark, Rhodesia, Germany, who worked alongside their British friends. The British group included Fleming, Leonard Colebrook, Carmalt Jones, Leonard Noon, who turned aside to explore the possibilities of immunizing sufferers from hay fever against the grass pollens which affected them ; John Freeman, who joined Noon in this effort and later included in his enquiry the whole field of allergic diseases ; the late Bernard Spilsbury who took over the pathological side, and Parry Morgan who did outstanding work in connection with getting partial rest for both lungs by pneumo-thorax therapy. Koch and Ehrlich had themselves visited the laboratory, and George Bernard Shaw and A. J. Balfour, who had been Prime Minister from 1902–1905, were among other personages strongly attracted to its atmosphere and to the intriguing nature of its undertakings.

Often during the midnight sessions Wright posed various principles of morality closely relevant to the work they were carrying on. Ought there to be " statistical evaluation of such heteregeneous clinical material ? " Ought they to rely on the " ' experimental method ', using their diacritical judgment upon the various impressions filtering through their minds ? " His preference was for the " experimental method " because he believed it was " less prone to error than the statistical one ", and he asserted that " the diacritical judgment, meaning the capacity to adjudicate on uncomfortable facts, was the highest quality of the mind, standing above all other gifts " ; more-over, he had a knack of drawing out those who had given only a passing thought to such questions, and of impressing upon them the need for meditating these problems.

Because of his reserve, Fleming was more listener than talker, but he weighed in silence the conflicting premisses and drew his own independent conclusions from them. "It's a pity I have not the gift of tongues," he has said, "it's worth more than anything else just to be able to talk. You know, with some men the words just flow out, and would charm a bird off a bush. But I was brought up wrongly for that." Yet Professor Pannett observes of him : "He never has liked to talk much, but on those occasions when he decides to give a judgment, you may be sure it will be highly perceptive, and there is no question of his shrewdness."

On the whole, he has never been unduly attracted towards metaphysical flights, towards the pursuit of abstractions. Discussing with a friend some scientist's interpretation of the Universe, of Space and Time, he remarked how little was really known about Space and Time. "Anyway," he added after a pause, indicating his watch, "this Time is quite good enough for me." Again, on his return from an important scientific conference abroad he wrote to this same friend : "I had a very good time but after two days among the super-scientists I was glad to escape to a less rarefied atmosphere."

On April 25th, 1908, Fleming appeared as part-author with Dr. Leonard Noon of an article called "The Accuracy of Opsonic Estimations", which was published in *The Lancet*. In it he and Noon made a rebuttal of certain charges by two doctors in the same journal, who offered figures on which "they question whether the tuberculo-opsonic index of tuberculous patients really does present any specific variation from the normal. "This," said Fleming and Noon, "is a blow aimed at the very basis of all opsonic work." Their reply, closely-reasoned and relying wholly upon the cogency of the facts they tellingly assemble, falls under four heads :

(1) A review of the methods by which the figures against them have been computed.
(2) Their own contention that the variations of normal sera are, in truth, small.
(3) Their own reasons for regarding the variations of tuberculous sera as large, and
(4) A criticism of the general methods upon which the opposing case rests.

In May, 1908, Fleming published the first paper ever to be issued under his name alone. It was a contribution to a special number of *The Practitioner*, devoted entirely to vaccine therapy and the opsonic method, and it was entitled : " Some Observations on the Opsonic Index with Special Reference to the Accuracy of the Method and to some likely Sources of Error." In a long exposition he covers ground he had partly covered in the previous paper written with Noon, and offers critics a much fuller answer. He writes :

" It is my intention . . . to confine myself to drawing attention to certain of the difficulties which an observer may encounter and the pitfalls he may meet (in the estimation of the opsonic index). At the same time I propose to bring forward some figures obtained at St. Mary's Hospital during the last eighteen months, which show that consistent results are obtained by the method.

" The opsonic index being the ratio of one serum to another which is taken as unity, depends for its accuracy on two factors :

    (*a*) The constancy of the control.
    (*b*) The accuracy of the estimation.

" Thus, however accurate the method, it would be useless trying to get results comparable from day to day, if the power of the control serum was a variable factor, and so, before discussing any question of the accuracy of the opsonic estimation, I think it would be wise to enquire into the question of the constancy of the control, and to this end I propose to adduce figures to show that, so far at least as the tubercle bacillus is concerned, the resistance of a healthy person is a very constant quality, and the variation is little more than can be accounted for by experimental error."

It is a thesis prepared with care, gaining its strength from the simplicity and directness with which it is presented. Throughout he keeps tenaciously to his point, building up his case with complete mastery over important detail, and an exemplary use of the statistical data upon which he establishes his case.

Nevertheless, at the beginning of the opsonic era a cardinal error had crept in. It had been assumed that the activity of the phagocytes themselves did not vary in sickness and in health. Therefore, the opsonic power of the serum was the all-important thing. It was then shown that the activity of the phagocytes does vary, but this somehow did not cause a re-examination of the previous assumption.

Thus the opsonic index in its early days had not given a true estimate of the patient's phagocytic power, but to have found that true index would have meant the testing of both phagocytes and serum. "Too much was attempted," writes Dr. Colebrook, "it was impossible to keep pace, we were often tired and uncritical after nights of work week in and week out. Yet the outstanding fact is that between 1903 and 1913, Wright's conception of immunization turned the direction of medical effort throughout the world."

Fleming himself has emphasised the most vital of his impressions during this phase of his career. "For years," he says, "I worked at phagocytosis so I could never forget the importance of the body's natural defences." It was an impression that was to have an unusually significant bearing upon future events.

Meanwhile, despite limitations of leisure, he contrived to keep up his sporting activities with the London Scottish. A photograph in the Regimental Gazette of June, 1908, captioned : "Marching to Victory", shows the team in kilts swinging along a country road. Fleming is at the head of the line bringing up the right flank of the column. He carries his rifle on his shoulder and is seen stepping out energetically, a short, compact figure with square-set shoulders. He is wearing a tunic buttoned to the throat, hose and white gaiters, the familiar Tam O'Shanter is on his head and his brasses gleam in the sun.

On that June day the Scottish shooting team, to which he belonged, won the *Daily Telegraph* Cup at Bisley. Later he was to say of the occasion :

"Once before I was proud of a little publicity when in 1908 the *Daily Graphic* published a photograph of our winning *Daily Telegraph* team headed : 'First in Skill and Endurance'. In those days the *Daily Telegraph* Cup was taken seriously by the Scottish and it consisted of a forced march of twelve miles from Weybridge to Bisley followed by a rapid shoot. It took place on the first Saturday in May and in 1908 the day was very hot.

"As we marched along we passed many men who had fallen

out from other teams, on Horsell Common we found all that was left of the Life Guards team fallen out on the roadside.

"The march was a wonderful illustration of the excellence of the kilt as a marching uniform, for we were the only team to arrive complete and in time, and I remember our skipper made us smarten ourselves up just as we arrived and marched up to the firing point in true Scottish style."

Two days later he sat for his M.B., B.S. examination, and once again regimental doings are curiously if more lightly interwoven with medical matters.

In his own words : " The episode (the march and the firing) was of immediate use to me, for on the very next Monday I sat for the final M.B. and there was a question on the ' relative humidity of the air and its effect on human exertions '. As I knew little or nothing about this, I told the examiners of the story of Saturday's march and compared the kilt with trousers, with the result that I got honours in that subject." He must have told them to some purpose unless, of course, as he himself humorously contends, " the examiner was a Scotsman ".

CHAPTER VI

FIRST DISCOVERIES

BY LION-HEARTED devotion to his work, through excessive and wearying hours, the fledgling bacteriologist was fast maturing into a notable craftsman, directed by a mind constantly attuning itself to penetrate a world of infinitesimal realities, whose enigmatic existence was called into being by the magnifying power of a microscope's lens. Until " the ascending process of well-being was fractured by a crime at Sarajevo ", as the historian H. A. L. Fisher has put it, there were rich and intense days, remembered by their moments of exhilaration, their excitements and expectations, when again and again hope soared and then sank to earth, when head and hands grew expert, when eyes grew keener, and the claws of imagination were sharpened on the newly-grown tree of knowledge pushing its way up in Wright's laboratory. The mind was being prepared, it was familiarizing itself with bacteriological lore. Yet from among the paraphernalia of the laboratory steps the man, momentarily at one with the more ordinary doings of his fellows, momentarily as unconcerned as they with such remote mysteries.

Fleming's old regimental friend, Robin Bailes, tells of their original meeting, which took place a few years before the First World War, while they were both enjoying an hour or two of relaxation : " I had not long joined the regiment and I was at the range, firing for the first time, when a quiet-voiced man knelt down beside me and began to give me some hints. Clearly he had been at pains to study the business and knew its ins and outs thoroughly. As he walked away, I turned to an N.C.O. and asked who he was. ' That's Senior Private Fleming,' came the answer. The stricter etiquette of the army in those days kept me from associating freely with him right away ; after all, he had been in a long time and I was a newcomer, but in due course we became friendly. To us all he was Alec, or sometimes Sandy, so you can guess the colour of his hair."

During this period also he began a friendship with the painter, Ronald Gray, only brought to its close when Gray died in the winter of 1951. At the time Gray, who was suffering from a tuberculous knee, was staying with friends and it was decided that he should consult Dr. Alexander Fleming, " one of Almroth Wright's brilliant young men ", so they invited Fleming to lunch with them. When he arrived they were surprised to meet a shy, rosy-faced Scotsman, even younger in appearance than they had imagined. They were attracted to him at once by his retiring demeanour, his matter-of-fact address, and by the complete absence in him of the conventional suavities, or the over-accomplished professional manner. Behind his directness and simplicity, they sensed a penetrating mind, capable of seizing without delay the essentials of any problem confronting it, and they could see that he was unafraid of expressing his real opinions.

Among the guests at lunch that day was the writer, George Moore, and during the course of the meal, Moore suddenly announced that he had " discovered " the Bible, and began to dwell on the wonder and colour of the tales in it. While communicating his raptures to the others, he referred to the Book of Ezekiel, which he insisted upon pronouncing as Ezkiel.

" Ez*e*kiel," corrected Fleming, making one of his rare interpolations, and hardly looking up from his plate.

" Ezkiel," said Moore for the second time, with more emphasis, recovering from his displeasure at this interruption and continuing.

" Ez*e*kiel," Fleming again corrected impassively, still entirely unconcerned by the effect on Moore who was looking quite taken aback and flushed ; he was certainly not accustomed to such contradictions, especially from apparently undistinguished strangers.

" I chuckled to myself," said Gray, " Moore could be so pompous on occasions ! On the other hand Fleming wasn't the man you could impress by the trappings of greatness ; he could never sacrifice his independence of outlook to the artificialities of convention. Look at him to-day, famous, loaded with honours, yet he never tries to be great. He simply goes on being what he always was. That's why he *is* great I suppose." When Fleming was knighted and Gray wrote to congratulate him, he received this answer : " Thanks for your nice letter. The Lord knows what my new form of address is. It does not change until I go to Buckingham Palace, and then I suppose it will be simply, Sir Alexander. Isn't this a funny world."

At their meeting he agreed to take Gray in hand. " I think I can help you," he said, and was as good as his word. After protracted treatment by vaccine therapy, followed by Swedish exercises and massage, Gray was cured.

It was an encounter promising unusual exchanges between two contrasting personalities belonging to contrasting worlds. As a small boy Gray had received a pat on the head from Carlyle and had grown up in time to savour the *mots* of Whistler and Wilde on the wing through the town, the piquancy of the *Yellow Book*, the unhastening urbanities that the witty Max Beerbohm spread over the scene. His heyday coincided with the fabulous era of Chelsea, where he was born and bred ; he mixed with the painters who made it so and became one of them almost as a matter of course. " The sacred emblems of Chelsea ", writes Max Beerbohm of the period, " were sold in the fashionable toy-shops, its reverently chanted creeds became the patter of the *boudoirs*. The old Grosvenor Gallery, that stronghold of the few, was verily invaded. Never was such a fusion of delighted folk as at its private views . . . And Walter Sickert spread the latest *mot* of ' the Master ', who, with monocle, cane and tilted hat, flashed through the gay mob anon."

Yet the eighteen-nineties, whose spirit carried over into the subsequent decades, had something else to offer than the so-called *fin-de-siècle* and the new hedonism ; indeed, its bias was more towards regeneration than towards the supposed degeneracy through which it sought to protest against the settled monotonies of the age. Into this context the renaissance in medicine led by Wright and his colleagues fitted well, and accordingly received its share of public attention. After all, the medical researcher, immersed in his dreams of man's greater physical well-being was not so far removed from the artist set on transmitting a saner, more beautiful vision of life's possibilities.

As a result of his association with Gray, Fleming was elected a member of the Chelsea Arts Club, where he found himself among men who, like him, were preoccupied with matters beyond the comfortable conventions or the importance of appearances. He found the *milieu* sympathetic because like them he had a creative gift, only he had turned it towards scientific investigation. Moreover, he has always underlined the kinship between artist and scientist who shared the common factor of creative vision.

It was not long before another painter sought his aid. He was stricken with sciatica, and no doctor had so far seemed able to bring him relief. " I think I can do something for you," Fleming told him, and treated him successfully. But the story did not end there. One day that same painter got into a railway carriage to find in it a man tormented by sciatica. " I've been to every doctor under the sun," this man (who turned out to be the governor of a London hospital) complained, " but none of them has been able to do anything for me."

" Well, you haven't been to the one doctor who can do something for you," the painter replied, and gave him Fleming's name. Some time later a car drew up outside the painter's studio and out of it stepped his companion of the train journey. He was erect and he walked without difficulty. " I've come to thank you for having given me the name of the doctor who really did do something for me," he said.

Gray, who had no admiration for what was being acclaimed as " modern art ", made up his mind to show it up, so he once persuaded Fleming to paint a picture in the currently fashion-able idiom for the purposes of exhibition. Entering into the spirit of things, he produced a view of the Children's Ward at St. Mary's, while Gray emerged with a canvas he thought would quite satisfy admirers of the cult. What is more, he persuaded the proprietor of a gallery to hang their efforts, under appropriate pseudonyms, alongside contributions of artists both British and foreign, who were then enjoying a tremendous vogue.

The critics accepted their pictures as genuine and praised them enthusiastically, until somehow the story of the hoax got about. The critics were naturally angry at having been taken in, and one infuriated contributor arrived to remove his canvases. He was somehow dissuaded and peace was at last restored after the recriminations, but Gray was hugely delighted with the success of his scheme and felt he had thoroughly exposed the fad for so-called modern art, and vindicated his opinion that it should not be taken seriously.

Though he is keenly interested in art, Fleming would be the last to claim for himself any skill as a painter, yet oddly attracted to the bizarre, he amuses himself in his laboratory by " painting " in a totally unorthodox fashion, using for pigments germ cultures which, when grown in an incubator, produce vivid colours. These he works into designs and into pictorial compositions. " It's quite simple," he says, " all you need is to get the right cultures, put them on paper with a brush, shove the lot in the incubator and there you are." One of his " bacterial " pictures is of a ship on fire, portrayed in brilliant reds and sombre violets, but his colleagues maintain that his greatest success came when he managed to reproduce the Union Jack. To them the results of his hobby are known as " Fleming's bacterial rock gardens ", and they tell how a certain Very Important Personage who, when shown the " bacterial rock gardens " during a visit to St. Mary's Hospital, was heard to remark more loudly than intended to an escort : " Yes, but what good are they ? "

Sometimes there were light-hearted expeditions out of town with his laboratory friends. A snapshot in which he is seen lying on an iron bedstead in his pyjamas, a cigarette between his fingers, is a reminder of a week-end at a Dorset cottage with Wright, Colebrook, Noon, Freeman, and an American colleague of those days. He does not in that picture look like a rising young bacteriologist, but rather like " one of those six gentlemen who don't look a bit like gentlemen ", as local village report had it.

They had walked along the sea-shore one afternoon, scatter-
ing as they progressed, when suddenly they found themselves
caught by the encroaching tide which had come in unnoticed.
Five of the party assembled to discuss what they should do,
but though they shouted and searched they could not find
Fleming who was missing. There was nothing for it but to
scramble up the steep cliff-side, so, wondering what had
become of him, they began their disagreeable climb. When
they reached the cottage they found him seated by the fire,
calmly making toast. But, like King Alfred, he had burned
it. Impolite comments and strong language were thrown at
his head. It was just like him to notice the tide coming in,
they said ; but why had he not tried to warn them ? Why
had he silently gone away? And to cap it all, he had burned
the toast and delayed their tea. . . . Unruffled, he started
making a fresh supply of toast. . . .

The extent of his activities outside the laboratories is shown
in an issue of the *St. Mary's Hospital Gazette* of June 1909. On
one page his name appears as a member of an executive committee set up to raise funds for the purchase of a sports ground
for the hospital ; on another he is given as a member of the
Rifle Club Committee, and below this entry is the record of a
shooting competition in which he had the top scores. In yet
another place, a paragraph headed *Sancta Maria Lodge* reads :
" Messrs. Daniels, Fleming and Webster were balloted for and
initiated into Freemasonry. A banquet was afterwards held
and attended by forty-three brethren and visitors, followed
by a musical entertainment." This event took place on
Tuesday, June 8th, 1909, at the Imperial Restaurant, Regent
Street, London. It was for him the beginnings of a life-long
association with Freemasonry, and of progress towards elevated
office in that movement.

1909 was an important year and the June issue of the *Gazette*
contains other references to him, which concern his professional
achievements. Under " Notes by the Editor " there is a
prophetic comment inspired by his success in the Final Fellowship Examination of the Royal College of Surgeons : " Mr.
Fleming, who was recently bracketed for the Gold Medal at
the M.B., B.S., and who seems to have merely taken the

Fellowship in his stride, is one of Sir Almroth Wright's most enthusiastic followers, and we see great distinction for him in the future." Thirty-seven years later, in the library of the Royal College of Surgeons, Lincoln's Inn, London, he was presented with the Gold Medal of that body, which, forty-nine years previously had been presented to Lord Lister and had not been awarded since. When he came to make a speech, he gave an amusing account of the Fellowship exam which he had sat in 1909. "Though my interests had by then already veered in the direction of bacteriology," he said, " I felt that having achieved the Primary, it would be a pity to allow so much effort and expense to be wasted ! "

He had then not yet reached his twenty-eighth birthday, but had carried off the highest distinctions his profession could offer. There were indeed grounds for confident predictions about his future. Moreover, the first apprentice years had now passed, the mental garnerings of an initial phase were ready for translation into action. He had tutored himself in the technical procedures of the laboratory, had assimilated the elements of which its unique atmosphere was blended, had habituated himself to its routines and had developed both the thrust and the poise of mind which would enable him to complete the passage towards maturity. And amid the intensity of labour, the mundane exchanges with colleagues intermingled with the bursts of debate and conversation about serious topics, he had to seek some still centre, some *punctum indifferens* for the serener contemplation of Nature as he observed its unsuspected and infinitely diversified operations.

The intensity of labour and the contemplation of its yield, they were two, yet they were one and indivisible, motivated by the will. " . . . Action, and work," Pasteur said, " always follow will, and work is almost always accompanied by success. These three things, will, work and success, divide between themselves all human existence ; will opens the door to brilliant and happy careers ; work allows one to pass through these doors, and once arrived at the end of the journey, success comes to crown one's efforts." The assets of a fine intellect marshalled by a formidable will had so far carried Fleming along his unbroken march of success ; the set of his face showed the presence of will, not even a shy exterior, an economy with words, could hide it. " If you ask me how to be successful," he has himself said over and over, " I would say—work, work and work again." He repeatedly gives it as the indispensable ingredient of success.

Work was to reveal to him that Nature must be understood, that its " wonderful powers ", which had so impressed him, must be encouraged in moments of enfeeblement to participate more completely in the process of recovery from disease. Time was to reveal to him that his faith in the body's natural defences, which had grown stronger and stronger with the passing years, had not been misguided. The human organism in combat with microbes had immense resources waiting to be tapped so that it could be assisted towards a full performance of its functions.

Meanwhile he had swung into action ; two fruitful pieces of research resulted, both of which had their practical application in medicine. In April 1909, he published a paper in *The Lancet* entitled : " The Etiology of Acne Vulgaris And Its Treatment by Vaccines ". The dictionary says that acne is a pimple, a disease marked by pimples, but this common or garden complaint causes embarrassment and a sense of inferiority among those who suffer from it, especially younger men and women. It has even been known to bring more serious psychological disturbances in its train. Until then, it had been held that it was caused by a staphylococcal infection, but Fleming's conclusions indicated different origins. " I here propose to set forth some investigations I have carried out on the bacteriology of the acne vulgaris," he writes, " which seem to show that this condition is not simply one of staphylococcic infection, but is largely due to a specific bacillary infection."

It was this acne bacillus, he contended, which gave rise to pustulation, but his careful investigations demonstrated also that, for purposes of treatment, patients fell into three separate classes. By using well-selected vaccines their condition could be relieved, but microscopical examination was important " before vaccine treatment is embarked upon in order that some certainty may be arrived at as to which class the patient belongs."

At this juncture he ventures his thoughtful opinion that, " we may take it as definitely proved now that in localized infection, when one inoculates the patient with appropriate doses of a carefully prepared vaccine derived from the infecting organisms one obtains a beneficial effect ". Science can rarely be hastened, for the most part it moves at its own decreed pace. In pursuit of the hopes held out by this therapeutic method they may not yet have enjoyed those intoxicating moments that come with the highest fulfilment, but in the barren landscape of medicine, which had troubled Wright, there had appeared the contenting sight of a good corner of growth, fostered by them.

In the following month, Fleming published a paper in *The Lancet* on "A Simple Method of Serum Diagnosis of Syphilis ". This disease was normally diagnosed by the use of the " Wassermann reaction ", a most complex test which, if properly executed, proved whether the person whose blood was under examination was infected with it or not. He modified this test, making it, in his own words, " much easier in performance ".

" The test which I will describe ", he wrote, " is exactly the same in its explanation as the original Wassermann reaction, but some of the complications of the original test are here avoided. The reaction may be used for diagnosis or as an indication for cessation of treatment. The method described is a clinical method, requiring only the preparation of a suitable tissue extract and an elementary knowledge of laboratory method. The reaction is positive in almost all cases of syphilis in the secondary and tertiary periods and in congenital syphilis. In primary syphilis the reaction may fail to appear. In cases after treatment the reaction may be negative, probably indicating the disappearance of the infection. The only disease I have met giving positive results, apart from syphilis, is leprosy."

The very simplicity of his method caused it to be treated with some reserve, but in fact it did exactly what he claimed it would do. " He has always shown a marked preference for

simple methods and simple apparatus ", his colleagues say ;
" such is his nature that elaborate procedures have no appeal
for him." It is a preference that has remained. Many years
later, in paying tribute to a distinguished fellow-scientist, Jules
Bordet, he declared : " The essence of Bordet's work is simplicity : simplicity of attitude and simplicity of technique. He
is always very sceptical about fantastic theories which have not
been adequately supported by the facts of experiment." It is
noticeable that he has selected the quality of simplicity for
his praise, that it commands his special admiration. Indeed,
all he has said of Bordet could well be said of him.

His account of one of the ways in which he has conducted
the experiments in connection with his modified test for
the diagnosis of syphilis is touched with a certain buoy-
ancy, a confident delight in the adept use of laboratory
devices :

" . . . a series of small test-tubes are made from a glass tube
by drawing it out in a blow-pipe at intervals of one inch. These
lengths are now sealed off at each end and divided in the middle
so that two small tubes remain each about half an inch long
and sealed at one end. These tubes are set upright in some
adhesive material (plasticine is most excellent material for the
purpose), in two rows, exactly like a company of soldiers, drawn
up in two ranks, each rear rank tube covering one of the front
rank. Each pair of tubes (one front and one rear rank) will now
correspond with the sample of the serum to be tested. A pipette
must now be made to measure the volumes of the fluids to be
used. . . . "

A pressing creative energy baulks at the set pattern, the
ready-made ; it drives him to employ his imagination and
make anew after his fashion. In his laboratory, his own
free kingdom, he revels in his technical virtuosity, in pulling
his technical rabbits out of the hat, and in painting his "bacterial " pictures as the mood for his own kind of entertainment
comes over him. When he carries this mood out of the
laboratory, it leads him to challenge an opponent to a round
of golf played with a single club, to spend hours improvising
fascinating games for the diversion of a small child, or to set
out to catch fish (leaving at home the finest rods) with what

has been described as " a bent pin at the end of a string attached to any old bit of stick ". Sometimes he will invite friends to stay with him at his place in the country and will prepare a special welcome for them by growing flowers laid out in the shape of their initials. These are lighter outlets for an overflowing imagination almost wholly directed into the service of scientific enquiry and felicitously expressing itself in the beauties of experiment, in a philosophy inclined to be pragmatic, its values transmuted and concerned with the practical bearing of things upon human interests.

1909 was a conspicuous time in the history of medicine, for in the August of that year, Paul Ehrlich, injected six rabbits, already in an advanced state of syphilis, with a solution of his 606 compound. The rabbits recovered and Ehrlich was convinced that he had in his hands a remedy not only for laboratory animals but for humans. He formally announced the discovery of Salvarsan (606) at a Medical Congress at Wiesbaden in April 1910. It was more than just an announcement of a cure for an evil disease ; as Dr. William Haynes has put it : " Paul Ehrlich's discovery created a new class of weapons against many deadly diseases, raising anew the hope of our ultimate victory over all germ diseases. For with Salvarsan the modern science of chemotherapy was born." Chematherapy was indeed a word of Ehrlich's own coining.

A strange caprice of destiny ordained that the world's first chemotherapeutic substance should, in England, be used at St. Mary's Hospital before it was used anywhere else, and by the man who was to carry Ehrlich's dream of a *therapia sterilisans magna* far beyond the great opening chapter that he had written. " Ehrlich introduced Salvarsan," Fleming has stated, " and sent some over to St. Mary's. It was my good fortune to use it, and the extraordinary dramatic effect it had on syphilitic lesions made an enormous impression on me who had for years been accustomed to the slower and more leisurely effect of vaccine therapy on septic and other infections." Together with his colleague, Leonard Colebrook, he published an article in *The Lancet* of June 1911, " On the use of Salvarsan in the Treatment of Syphilis."

" Much has already been written on the subject of the treatment of syphilis by means of Salvarsan or, as it is popularly known ' 606 '. The chemical constitution of the new remedy and the methods by which it was discovered have been so often described that it would be mere waste of time to allude to them here, but we think it may be of some value to place on record the results we have obtained by the use of the drug during the last nine months.

" Through the kindness of Professor Ehrlich, we were enabled to use the new remedy since August of last year. At first all our injections were made intramuscularly, but later, owing to a letter we received from Professor Ehrlich, we changed the method to an intravenous one. The intravenous method has many advantages. It is much less painful, and enables the patient to get about with perfect comfort in much less time than the older method. Its effect is quicker and more certain, and recurrences are less common."

They conclude :

" Whether the new drug will displace mercury in the treatment of syphilis remains to be seen, and we do not venture to express any opinion on this subject. It, however, certainly has a remarkable effect in causing the lesions to disappear, and especially is this seen in some cases which have resisted mercurial treatment. Much has been made of the dangers inherent in the administration of the drug, but so far we have not seen the slightest trace of the evil effects which have been written about in any case which has been injected intravenously."

About forty years had gone by since Pasteur had told the *Académie des Sciences* that the cause of " transmissible, contagious and infectious diseases resides essentially and solely in the presence of microscopic organisms." He disposed of the idea of spontaneous generation, declaring that : " We must abandon all those opinions which are fatal to medical progress . . . " The germ theory of disease was established. At Pouilly-le-Fort in 1881 he proved for all time that animals could be protected against infective diseases with vaccines, and Immunology became the heading of a quickly-filling section in the chronicle of medicine. Now Chemotherapy had arrived, a new heading to a new section of that chronicle, recording a single episode in which the union of biological and chemical forces had brought propitious results. Till then the edifice of medicine had rested largely upon the foundations provided by Pasteur and his French school, but the accomplishment of the German, Ehrlich, with his conception of a systematic attack on disease by the use of specific chemicals for the destruction of specific bacteria, began to engage the interests of medical researchers.

Somehow, Pasteur had seen beyond chemical specifics for the treatment of disease ; he thought in terms of prevention rather than cure, of acquired immunity by artificial means. Stimulated by Pasteur's ideas and by Metchnikov's theory of phagocytosis, Wright, Fleming and others at St. Mary's Hospital were striving to realise a conception expressed in Wright's aphorism that " the physician of the future will be an immunisator." In 1908 Wright had declared :

" Already in my first paper on the treatment of staphylococcus infections by the therapeutic inoculation of staphylococcus vaccines, I suggested we had in vaccine therapy a general therapeutic method which would be applicable to the treatment of all kinds of localized bacterial infections. In my next publication on therapeutic inoculation, I made bold to predict that the physician of the future would be an immunisator. Already these anticipations are justifying themselves. I do not know that there is anyone who has made a trial of vaccine therapy in connection with local bacterial diseases who is not satisfied with its efficacy as a therapeutic measure, and the day when the physician will be an immunisator is, I think, perceptibly nearer."

Unhappily, the great day of consummation which had seemed nearer did not come. Dr. Leonard Colebrook tells why :

" To use this method of blood examination as a routine guide to the dosage of vaccines was not practicable because of the labour involved and the many technical difficulties ; Wright himself later regarded it as inadequate."

Or, as Dr. Carmalt Jones has expressed it : " Only a man of Wright's tremendous personality could have kept a team together working till all hours without a single order from him ; the work was intensely laborious, and though of value in the hands of experts, could not be adapted for general use."

Fleming himself, reviewing the history of vaccine therapy and the opsonic index in after years, has said :

" . . . Louis Pasteur established for all time the principle of
active immunity by means of bacterial vaccines. Pasteur's work
was carried on entirely with living vaccines and, except for
rabies, was concerned only with animal diseases. Living vaccines
have certain fairly obvious drawbacks in human medicine, and
the next advance was the use of prophylactic vaccines made from
killed cultures. This step was intimately associated with the
name of our great countryman and my own master, Sir Almroth
Wright, who has advanced science in many ways, not the least of
which was the introduction of anti-typhoid vaccine, still
universally applied. The next step, the vaccine treatment of
established infections, was entirely due to Wright's initiative. It
began with the treatment of local staphylococcal infections of the
skin, but has now spread to many others.

"When I first started working at bacteriology in Wright's
laboratory in St. Mary's Hospital in 1906, vaccine therapy was
in its infancy, and there were great hopes that by its means all
bacterial infections could be controlled. Now, some thirty-three
years afterwards we can look back and congratulate ourselves
that although all these hopes have not been completely fulfilled,
and although we are far off finality in our knowledge and practice
of active immunization, in many types of infection a great
measure of relief can be given to patients by the intelligent use
of vaccines."

Yet, though tinged with disappointments, the fact remained
that wonderful things had been accomplished, wonderful contributions made to the total of medical knowledge. And in
the errors of those long days, vibrant with the play of splendid
aspirations, there were lessons to be learned. Fleming, with
the strength to be neutral when the formation of calm judgment demanded it, learned them. Errors mattered desperately
to a man, especially when he viewed them in retrospect and
could gauge how far he had benefited from their com-
mission.

They had established the need for precise bacteriological
diagnosis and had done much to dissipate the tenuous and
antiquated ideas of disease that had survived the past ; they
had fabricated a host of new laboratory devices which had
made the investigation of disease easier, and their achievements had made others see the need for laboratories if scientific
procedures in medicine were to replace the older guess-work
methods.

Summing up, Dr. Colebrook states :

" It is fair to say that the progress in immunization has so far chiefly been due to three pioneers : Jenner, Pasteur and Wright. Of them Wright contributed the most to our understanding of the subject.

" There was tremendous opposition from the High Priests of Harley Street, who were not pleased to be told that medicine must become applied bacteriology. . . .

" Finally, though new roads have opened up in the intervening forty years, Nature's primary defence mechanism against microbic disease, so far as is known, is that of phagocytosis, regulated largely by the opsonic effect of serum as Wright conceived it."

But while Wright, Fleming and others toiled for the realisation of their dreams, the end of an era was approaching, the death of an old time. They may not, however, have been aware of it, for it was given to few to forecast that in the golden August weather of 1914 stunning news would come which was to tear them away from their normal occasions and set them to urgent and special tasks for which their qualifications fitted them.

CHAPTER VII

THE BOULOGNE DAYS: 1914-1918

BRITAIN DECLARED war on Germany on August 4th, 1914, two days before Fleming's thirty-third birthday. He was then living at a flat in Clarence Gate Gardens where he and his family had been installed since 1906, and where they were still being looked after by their mother. The year previous he had taken consulting rooms in Devonshire Place which he shared with his friend, Professor Pannett, and had begun a specialist practice, though he continued to work in Wright's laboratories at the same time.

In the April of 1914 he had regretfully broken off his long association with the London Scottish Regiment. He was no longer No. 37, Private Fleming of the 14th Battalion as he had been since the regiment had become a territorial unit in 1908. Increasing work and increasing responsibilities had more and more intruded into his spare time. He had enjoyed long marches and annual camps, he had enjoyed the sport and the comradeship, he had been what his friend, Robin Bailes, described as " a good trencherman and one of the best footsloggers in the regiment." He had done the Bisley Fortnight, had fired for the King's Prize, and had been in teams which had competed for coveted shooting trophies. He was always to remember how he and his fellows had won the *Daily Telegraph* Cup, the first such important event carried off by a territorial unit ; the coolness of the swinging kilt in the heat of the day, the cheers as they strode up to the firing-point on time without a single man lost, the needling quarter of an hour's wait during which they rolled up their sleeves and dipped their arms in the puddle near which they lay to steady their muscles, the order to advance and fire. . . . Had he had the ample leisure in which to concentrate on his marksmanship, he might have been a really great shot instead of a very fine one. . . .

Perhaps it was one of those inexplicable interventions of chance that caused him to abandon his soldiering those few months before war came ; it was certainly lucky for the world, because the Scottish were soon in France and were cut to pieces at Messines. Who knows, had he remained with them he, too, might have been there. Now the regiment had been mobilized and a thousand men were at their headquarters in the Buckingham Palace Road—waiting. They had little with which to occupy themselves at the outset so he was asked to give them a talk. His unaffected delivery and his straight-forward language held his listeners as he spoke about matters of hygiene and about that subject of such concern to all infantrymen : the care of the feet. Many of them were his old comrades of the 14th Battalion, especially those of No. 4 Section, No. 8 Squad of H. Coy., to which he had belonged. The general impression was that the war would be a short, sharp encounter with a mighty battle of armies and navies for its shuddering climax ; few anticipated that nearly all the world would become enmeshed in its painfully slow agonies. Thus feelings burned high, nourished by an optimism, which veiled the undertones of melancholy.

But while many could be taught to fire at their enemies, few knew how to bring succour after their enemies had returned their fire and the wounded cried out for attention. Wright set out the unprecedented problems facing the doctors :

"In civilized conditions one may hope to get through life with a comparatively whole skin ; and, if a surgical operation is called for, aseptic precautions can be taken. Hence sepsis, whether as suppuration of wounds or 'blood poisoning', does not in ordinary life come into consideration as an appreciable risk. In war, wounds are, of course, in the programme. Also we have, in addition to wounds inflicted by the enemy, all manner of mechanical injuries—in particular badly blistered feet and raws. . . . Shrapnel wounds, wounds with comminution of bones, and all-extensive raws will almost inevitably become septic.

"Moreover it will often be impracticable to secure in field hospitals the ascepticity of operation wounds, and it will at any rate be impossible to keep them aseptic for any length of time.

"There is, in fact, one sanitary policy for peace and civilized surroundings, and another for war and uncivilized surroundings."

For the first time in the history of warfare high-explosives were in use, causing wound infections on a scale hitherto undreamt of; for the first time in the history of warfare also, the need for medical research had to be admitted. Fleming soon went to Boulogne, where a laboratory had been set up under the authority of Wright, who had been appointed a Colonel of the Army Medical Service. And with him were some of his colleagues from St. Mary's, including Dr. Colebrook, Dr. Parry Morgan and Dr. Freeman, while Dr. Carmalt Jones was also nearby, working in the hospital of a hutted camp at Wimereux. Except for a period when he returned home to work at St. Mary's Hospital, where the Medical Research Council had had wards set apart for the reception of severely wounded men, Fleming was at Boulogne. It was at Boulogne he carried out those important experiments which, according to Professor Pannett, were to make him, " the ardent, militant antagonist of antiseptics."

There Wright had taken a house in the Boulevard Daunau by the River Liane, and in it they all lived simply and without great ceremony. A laboratory had been improvised on the roof of the Casino, which had been the headquarters of a fencing club. When Fleming arrived, however, he says: " The labs. at first consisted of two subterranean bathrooms which were periodically flooded with sewage." Soon the halls of the Casino were lined with rows of wounded lying on stretchers placed close to each other. Most of them fretted in their mental distress, many of them endured pain beyond bearing. "Those who slept in that Boulogne house," says Dr. Colebrook, "will always remember the quiet, muffled tramp of soldiers passing through the night."

In hospital wards they saw men with bones in fragments, with muscles irreparably lacerated, with larger blood vessels and nerves severed. And overnight some of them would go ashen, pulses beating weakly, their torn limbs turning leaden, as hard as board and as cold to the touch as marble. These were the unmistakable signs of gas-gangrene. Amputations were hurriedly done but few survived; it was mortal within the space of hours. Too often they examined lesser injuries which, having encouraged hopes of recovery, became the centres of extending cellulitis, presaging septicæmia. And death. " We have in this war gone back to all the septic infections of the Middle Ages," declared the Director-General ot the Army Medical Service. If only they had possessed fuller knowledge ! As it was they might with Benassio in Balzac's *Country Doctor* have cried : " Mon Dieu, science cannot save him unless Nature works a miracle ! "

Professor Pannett has used the words, dour and reticent of Fleming. Yet this silent nature, incapable of self-dramatization or picturesque actions was none the less affected to the quick by the terrible powerlessness of medicine to help the stricken humans passing daily before his eyes in such numbers. It was a haunting problem that he and his colleagues sought to answer. How were they to deal with sepsis and end its fearful consequences ? Fleming has surveyed antiseptic methods from their beginnings and through the war years. Then, although chemicals were tried out in their varieties, they were found wanting. He says :

" Sepsis is no modern innovation, and during the centuries there is no doubt that the witch doctors, barbers, physicians and surgeons have used many remedies to combat sepsis. We need not seriously discuss anything that happened before there was some understanding of the nature of sepsis. Less than a century ago, Pasteur showed that putrefaction was caused by living organisms which did not arrive *de novo* but only by contamination with some infected material. This was an extraordinary advance, but looking back there seems no reason why this doctrine should not have been accepted after the experiments of Spallanzani.

" However, Pasteur did these experiments, and Lister (whose mind had been made receptive by years of vain fight against sepsis), before there was any real knowledge of bacteriology, accepted the teaching and used chemicals to prevent access of microbes in his operation wounds. Pasteur had shown that microbes gain access to sterile fluids from the air, so Lister used carbolic sprays to kill the microbes in the air around his operations. He also washed his hands and attempted to sterilize them with carbolic acid, and he sterilized his instruments and everything which touched the wound with carbolic acid. In this way he revolutionized surgery and showed that by the use of chemical antiseptics, operations could be performed with a reasonable certainty that the wound would heal without suppuration.

" He had succeeded but it was apparently a hard struggle

to convince the medical profession at large that his procedure was worth while.

" When I was a student people talked of Lister as a back number and antiseptic methods were completely out of date. Aseptic surgery had taken their place. But what was asceptic surgery ? Merely the substitution of one antiseptic for another ; heat for carbolic acid. Dressings and instruments were sterilized by heat, the surgeon's hands were encased in rubber gloves, and the air was kept pure by wearing of gowns and other sterile apparel, all ' sterilized by heat '. Lister's teaching is still true—microbes must be kept away from a wound. But while Lister by the use of antiseptics had succeeded in keeping operation wounds clean, there still remained the problem of the wound in which the infection had become established, and in which the microbes had invaded the surrounding tissue.

" Prior to the war, the surgeon gave most of his attention to aseptic methods, his great object being to exclude microbes from the wound. The question of how to deal with the bacteria after they were in possession was a problem of much less interest to him. I can remember in the days when I was first admitted to the surgical wards as a dresser, there were always a certain number of septic wounds which we were instructed to dress with this or that antiseptic, which stood in jars around the fire, and which we were told possessed great virtue as destroyers of microbes in the wound. These antiseptics were chiefly carbolic acid, mercury salts, and boric acid. The wounds were religiously dressed once or twice a day with these lotions, and although it was obvious that the antiseptic did not kill all the microbes in the wound, we were always told that it would kill many of them, and so the condition would be better than if no antiseptic were used. We applied some substance and next day the condition wasn't much different ; and we did it again until eventually the wound got well. There was a great deal of faith in that sort of treatment.

" Meanwhile, surgeons remained relatively complacent to sepsis until the 1914–18 war began. Then they were confronted with thousands of wounds all more or less septic and they resorted to chemicals to destroy these microbes. At the beginning of the war in 1914 all the old antiseptics were used in military hospitals, in just such a manner as when I started surgery. Carbolic acid, perchloride or biniodide of mercury, boric acid, and hydrogen peroxide were poured into septic wounds once or twice daily, either singly or in mixtures of two or more, according to the fancy of the medical officer.

" Very soon, however, campaigns were started in favour of particular antiseptics. Early in 1915, the merits of pure carbolic acid and two per cent iodine in spirit were tested. A certain number of cases were treated with these two chemicals at the

Front, and the patients were sent down to No. 13 General Hospital, where I had the opportunity of seeing the wounds and examining them bacteriologically. In the carbolic series there was a higher percentage of gas gangrene than in the general run of the wounded, while the iodine cases showed practically no difference from the cases treated in other ways. Soon after this, antiseptic pastes were advocated. The wound was plugged with the paste, but it soon appeared that in France, at any rate, the chief result of this method of treatment was to shut off all drainage, so that gas infections developed in a large number of cases. These pastes, therefore, very soon disappeared from the antiseptic armamentarium."

His experiments with these antiseptics which gained successive popularity left him under no misapprehensions whatsoever as to their effects in wounds ; they were all more harmful to the body's protective mechanisms than to the microbes they were intended to destroy. Describing the tests which confirmed his gathering scepticism, he states :

" . . . When we became concerned with septic wounds on a large scale, we did some experiments and made some observations on antiseptics. One of the most popular methods of antiseptic treatment was the Carrel-Dakin method. Dakin's fluid was put into the wound every two hours. (This was a solution of sodium hypochlorite.) I found that the potency of Dakin's fluid disappeared within ten minutes in a wound so that, for one hour and fifty minutes out of every two hours, there was no antiseptic in the wound. That may have been fortunate, but in any case it was a successful method of ' antiseptic ' treatment—at least, as successful as was possible in those days.

" But just because a product is labelled an antiseptic doesn't mean that it doesn't do something else. Dakin's fluid was really a poor antiseptic, but if Dakin's fluid is applied to a wound the amount of exudation from the walls of the wound increases considerably just as it does with hypertonic salt solutions which were also successful applications to septic wounds. Many people paid no attention to that.

" Then chemical antiseptics may affect the natural defences. This can be estimated by use of a contraption which I am rather fond of, called the ' slide cell '. Into a narrow cell you run blood, plus microbes, plus chemical. Now suppose you run in blood, plus about fifty staphylococci, along with a little salt solution. You get two or three staphylococcal colonies ; the blood kills the rest. Blood is a good killer of microbes so long as the leucocytes are intact. Then, as you put in carbolic acid, beginning with a weak solution and making it gradually stronger and stronger, more and more staphylococci appear. At a dilution of one in six hundred and forty of carbolic acid, all the staphylococci grow. The antiseptic, then, has made the blood a first-class culture medium. (In fact, it is one way of doing a blood culture.)

" Carbolic acid has this effect because it kills the cells, the polynuclear leucocytes, in a concentration at which it won't injure bacteria. By this method I found carbolic acid and all the other common antiseptics used in former days killed leucocytes more easily than they killed microbes. They were not likely to be very successful in the body—and they weren't !

" After ' Carrel ' treatment came the era of B.I.P.P. This was a paste made by mixing iodoform, bismuth and paraffin, and it obtained many supporters. It was, however, combined with very careful surgical treatment of the wound, and in connection with its use another factor was introduced into wound treatment, in that after treatment with the paste the wound was not touched for a considerable time, thus obtaining complete rest for the part and so aiding the physiological activities of the body in combating infection. . . . It was reported to have an antiseptic action when placed in contact with tissues or tissue fluids ; but this we have never been able to demonstrate, and thus are forced to the conclusion that the paste is not a chemical antiseptic at all, but if it has any action in keeping down infection, it is due to some physical or physiological action.

" After B.I.P.P. came the dye-stuffs. . . . Browning recommended brilliant-green and more especially flavine, to which he attributed very remarkable properties as an antiseptic for use in septic wounds. Flavine differed from other antiseptics in that its bactericidal action was greater in a serous than in a watery medium. Browning maintained also that it killed all the common microbes found in wounds in a very high dilution, while it had little toxic effect on the tissues, as exemplified by leucocytes.

" Briefly, I found that it had a very slight antiseptic action on some of the microbes found in wounds. In pus also it had little bactericidal action, and it had a very destructive effect on the leucocytes. Browning's findings that it had little action on the leucocyte, while it had a powerful bactericidal action followed merely from the fact that he tested the action on leucocytes for a few minutes only, whereas the action on the microbes was tested on a minimal infection for twenty-four hours.

" Flavine also has a remarkable affinity for the walls of the wound and for the dressing, so that it is rapidly picked up and rendered inert by these walls and by the gauze pack. Its affinity for the dressing can be shown by the following simple experiment : A test tube is half filled with flavine 1-1000, and a tight-fitting cotton wool plug is slowly pushed down into it, until the fluid escapes above the plug. The first portion of the fluid which comes through the plug will be found to be absolutely without the yellow coloured flavine, showing that the cotton-wool has been able to remove the whole of this substance from the solution. . . .

"It was soon found in practice that when a wound was treated with flavine 1-1000 (the strength recommended) for more than a few days, all the reparative processes stopped, while the flavine did not sterilize the wound, so that for the continued treatment of septic wounds it was found quite unsuitable."

So Fleming, after proper scientific enquiry, proceeded to knock down one after the other the numerous Antiseptic Aunt Sallys which popped up their heads in turn to beg a favourable if transient acceptance. It is Shaw, perhaps, who has most bitingly dismissed the curious delusions of an era in medicine which was obsessed by the sport of microbe-hunting with chemicals of one sort and another for weapons, whose efficacy Fleming proved to be more than questionable. In the preface to *The Doctor's Dilemma*, he writes : " We are left in the hands of generations which, having heard of miracles much as St. Thomas Aquinas heard of angels, suddenly concluded that the whole art of healing could be summed up in the formula : Find the microbe and kill it. But doctors instinctively avoid all facts that are reassuring, and eagerly swallow those that make it a marvel that anyone could live three days in an atmosphere consisting mainly of countless pathogenic germs. They conceive microbes as immortal until slain by a germicide administered by a duly qualified medical man . . . In the first frenzy of germ-killing, surgical instruments were dipped in carbolic oil, which was a great improvement on not dipping them in anything at all and simply using them dirty ; but as microbes are so fond of carbolic oil they swarm in it, it was not a success from the anti-microbic point of view."

But it was not enough to put a finger upon the glaring inadequacy of chemical antiseptics, so Wright, Fleming and others plunged into the investigation of a problem which had survived Lister's day : that of killing bacteria which had already gained access to a freshly inflicted wound and had established an infection which invaded the tissues to a considerable depth. " We must first understand the physiological processes going on in the wound," Wright declared, " we do not yet understand them even in outline. It will be necessary to address ourselves to the task of discovering what goes on in the wound and to follow up its biological evolutions." It was Fleming who made certain brilliant observations at No. 13 Base Hospital in Boulogne and gave reasons why war wounds became so rapidly infected. These he published in *The Lancet* of September 1915 under the title, " On the Bacteriology of Infected Wounds."

Bullet and shell wounds were prone to infection because " in practically all cases the projectile had to pass through the clothing of the soldier, and in its passage it gathers up mud or pieces of mud-covered clothing and plants such material deep in the wound. It is common to find in these wounds pieces of clothing, sometimes of considerable size."

Next he set out to determine the relationship between the infections in the wounds and the bacteria on the clothing, by examining pieces of clothing cut off from places that could not have become contaminated by discharge from the injury itself. After testing twelve such samples of clothing he obtained interesting results : the bacillus of Welch showed in ten out of the twelve samples ; one in three showed the presence of the tetanus bacillus, which was significant because of the prevalence of the disease at that moment, while streptococcus occurred in five and staphylococcus in two.

The bacillus of Welch (named after the American bacteriologist who described it in 1892, but which he himself called *bacillus aerogenes capsulatus*), is a gas-forming microbe, an anaerobe, since it does not grow in the presence of air. This microbe and the tetanus bacillus live in the intestines of men and beasts, or in soil which has been manured with animal excrement, the former constantly to be seen in human fæces and the latter in the defecations of some animals.

Fleming thus demonstrated that the primary infection of wounds was a fæcal one.

Moreover, he showed that secondary infections of wounds

from the skin were almost inevitable, since the area surrounding the wound was covered with a thick dressing into which discharges had soaked. " Putrefactive poultices " they had been termed.

In collaboration with the late Dr. S. R. Douglas and Dr. Colebrook, Fleming studied the question of bacterial symbiosis in wound infections, and the deductions they made from their tests threw light upon aspects of that tragic condition, gas gangrene.

Bacterial symbiosis has a formidable sound in the layman's ear, but it means simply that one species of microbe may assist the multiplication of another when the two are grown in the same culture medium. The three of them were able to demonstrate that an assortment of microbes, which the bacteriologist expects to meet in wounds, and in themselves unlikely to provoke serious complications, became suddenly sinister in their power to stimulate the growth of bacteria that were dangerous. For example, Fleming showed that a certain gas-forming microbe (called Bacillus perfringens) increased in numbers when in the company of staphylococci, streptococci and certain other bacteria which usually inhabit wounds.

Thus they compared the behaviour of this microbe to a high explosive, which remained harmless until the explosive action was started by a detonator, for the microbe was ' set off ' by symbiosis or ' microbic mutual aid ', and when the alkilinity or antitryptic power of the blood serum was neutralized, thereby inducing gas gangrene.

During the course of their experiments they found also that the bacillus of Welch, which could set up gas-gangrene, although it was an anaerobe and unable to grow in the presence of air, did in fact grow under aerobic conditions in fluid media, provided that some porous substance like a piece of potato or asbestos wool had been added to it. From this observation, therefore, they shrewdly inferred that it could thrive when—as frequently happened—a piece of the soldier's clothing had become embedded in a wound.

Then Wright and Fleming persisted in the search for information about gas-gangrene. They maintained that a patient suffering from this disease succumbed to acid intoxication or acidaemia, because it caused a grave reduction in the alkilinity of the blood. Already Wright had proved that the bacillus of Welch when cultivated in serum rendered it acid, and he and Fleming now asked themselves whether minor gas-gangrene bacilli also produced acid in the serum and whether they grew more freely in serum of diminished alkilinity.

To answer this question they performed a carefully planned test. They planted four portions of serum with four such microbes in quantity ; they next took ten sub-volumes of each implanted serum to which they added some weakened sulphuric acid, diluting the control portion of the serum to an equivalent extent. They then filled the separate portions into narrow tubes, excluding the air by a layer of melted vaseline, and these were incubated. The amount of gas evolved could be taken as the measure of growth since it drove the vaseline plugs a certain distance up the tubes. The results showed that these subordinate gas-gangrene bacilli behaved like the bacillus of Welch : they found it hard to grow in normal serum, but grew better and better as its alkilinity was blunted off. It seemed probable, therefore, that when a battle-weary man suffered serious injury, the devitalized muscle, which tended to elaborate carbonic and lactic acid, encouraged the development of the gas-gangrene bacillus, especially when cut off from its blood-supply by trauma, tourniquet, or ligature, or by collapse of the circulation.

Of the symptoms of this grotesque malady they have written most vividly : " We have, in the large majority of cases, well marked air-hunger ; in some we have quite classical air-hunger ; and where we find this symptom absent it is, we may suggest, because the agonal cold is already creeping up over the gas-gangrene patient. In such circumstances, with internal respiration practically extinguished, carbon dioxide pouring into the blood and further acid products excluded, air-hunger is ruled out . . . The constitutional symptoms common to all forms of acidosis would seem to be two : first, air-hunger, which though an outstanding symptom when muscular exercise puts a strain on the respiratory mechanism, may easily cease to be apparent when the patient is at complete rest and the internal respiration is cut down. The second important clinical feature of acidosis is that the life of the patient or experimental animal in this condition hangs on a thread. We leave our gas-gangrene patient for an hour and we come back and find him dead . . . But before death (as they describe) he would display, a sallow, earthy aspect; and a purplish mottling of the skin would mark an advance wave of diminishing alkilinity."

Sometimes the surgeon's knife could stem the dire progress of the condition; lymphagogic salt solution could be applied locally to the wound, and for general treatment the intravenous injection of bicarbonate of soda to try and restore the alkilinity of the blood. In giving their account of the administration of such injections, Wright and Fleming emphasize a certain traditional hostility between investigator and practitioner and deplore the risks of distortion involved in the communication of their laboratory findings to the persons who will apply them in practice.

Of such incompatibilities, Fleming must have taken good note; he was to experience them during his career, especially at the moment when penicillin passed into general use. Meanwhile they declared:

"It is the bane of scientific research that if ever there is suggested by it a therapeutic measure, that procedure is, despite all its advocates may do, represented as either a complete panacea or a measure which disappoints legitimate expectation. If a little quiet thought were given to the therapeutic problems in question all this would be avoided. Here, for instance, in connection with the treatment of the acidosis of gas gangrene, one ought not to have to preface one's recommendations of alkiline injections by a formal confession of faith that the toxaemia (poisoning) of gas gangrene must be something more than an acidosis. Again, even if one were supposed to believe that we are, in the toxaemia of gas gangrene, confronting a simple acidosis, one would wish to be credited with the power of seeing that one cannot in a severe acidaemic case, where the whole salt content of the blood has been profoundly altered, hope by an injection of bicarbonate of soda to bring about a restoration of its integrity . . . ."

As it turned out, the effectiveness of alkali therapy was never fully assessed, for in the press of events there was hardly time for the intense researches required to make such an assessment. It was sometimes successful and sometimes not, but offered a means of dealing with acidosis until later in the war when interest veered towards the use of specific serums for combating the toxins generated by gas-gangrene microbes.

Meanwhile the stream of experiments flowed on, Fleming and his colleagues were carrying out to some effect Wright's injunction that they should " discover what goes on in a wound and follow up its biological evolutions." Already in 1915, Fleming was able to point to the extraordinary degree of phagocytosis that occurred in wound discharges, indicating the vehement resistance to infection put up by Nature. "The severity of these wound infections," he said, " is merely the result of the very extensive destruction of the tissues by the projectile, thus furnishing an admirable culture medium for the bacteria out of reach of the natural protective forces of the body, and if it were possible for the surgeon to remove completely this dead tissue, I am quite sure the infections would sink into insignificance."

Not long afterwards, new surgical procedures such as he mentioned were introduced, which obscured the effects of the antiseptics themselves, but in that phrase, " protective forces of the body " lived the soul of Fleming's disbelief in chemical antiseptics and their advocates. Highly versed in the behaviour of the phagocytes after years of vaccine therapy, it must have seemed incredible to him that natural processes should be so overlooked. " I want to draw your attention," he has said, " to a very powerful antiseptic we keep in the body—all of us—and which people are apt to forget ; that is, the body cells. We are apt to forget that we have lots of cells which can phagocyte bacteria, and after they pick them up, digest them and destroy them. It is by means of these that we probably get rid of most of our infections. Of course, just the picking up of a microbe by a cell doesn't mean that the microbe is dead. Most cells are greedy—at least, they can be very greedy—and they can pick up more than they can digest. (This characteristic is not confined to cells.) If cells ingest too many microbes, the microbes destroy the cells, not the cells the microbes. But don't forget that in the body we have these powerful mechanisms at work."

Instead of doubtful chemicals, therefore, Wright and his followers recommended the use of a five per cent salt solution, a lymphagogic solution, that brought into play osmotic forces, drew lymph out of the walls of the wound and ensured a free flow of exudate rich in anti-tryptic power, which was Nature's own immediate response to injury and infection. They also pressed for the early closure of wounds by surgical means.

In 1915 Wright on two occasions addressed the Royal Society of Medicine and put forward these then unusual views, at the same time avowing his belief that it was mistaken to sterilize wounds at the outset by applying antiseptics. He said :

> " It has been erroneously inculcated that every wound should be sterilized before closure ; and that, therefore, *primary suture* should be avoided and *secondary suture* undertaken only after a course of antiseptics. There is now no question, with respect to primary suture, that the wound taken after early surgical cleansing and resection is as good as sterile . . .
> " It has been taught that for the removal of sloughs from foul wounds chemical solvents are required. We have learned that sloughs can be removed by tryptic ferment set free from disintegrated leucocytes, and that the liberation of this ferment can be greatly accelerated by breaking down the leucocytes in the discharges with hypertonic saline solution."

Dr. Leonard Colebrook states that " the tone of these lectures were unprovocative, contained no personal attack and were legitimate reports upon a scientific investigation, embodying fair criticisms of opposing views which he sincerely believed prejudicial to the wounded."

Nevertheless, their publication raised acrid controversy, dividing the medical world against itself. The ultramontanes of doctoring clung to their faith in chemical antiseptics and were affronted by the propagation of what they considered a heresy. Sir William Watson Cheyne himself, endowed with all the prestige of his office as President of the Royal College of Surgeons, of his Fellowship of the Royal Society and of his youthful associations with the great Lister, wrote in the *British Journal of Surgery* urging a reversion to the Listerian practice of fifty years before and attacking Wright's contentions as a mixture of fact and fantasy.

Yet neither zealous partisanship nor the acrimony of the

ensuing polemics, exciting at the time and still entertaining to scan, were of little consequence as Wright hastened to note. It was of small moment whether one or other generalization should be adopted, whether one pet theory should be preferred to another, but it was of unsurpassed consequence that wounded men might have to pay for the decrees of exalted orthodoxy voiced to discredit new notions on the insecure grounds of their heterodoxy. His case for the use of the hypertonic saline rested upon the unequivocal results of laboratory experiments performed by him and by his fellow workers like Fleming. They had lived among men terribly mutilated by ravaging high-explosive, their minds darkened by the distress they witnessed, and they understood the unavoidable delays of the battlefield. Precious hours, sometimes days, were lost before a soldier who had been struck down could have his injuries treated with antiseptics, nor did the condition of these injuries improve with the passage of time, and the possibilities of disinfection kept waning.

As the fume and fret of dispute abated, it seemed that Cheyne had little first-hand experience of wounds and scanty clinical experiment of their treatment, while Wright, in the exacerbated circumstances of controversy, gave the impression that antiseptics could in no circumstances disinfect a wound, a standpoint he subsequently modified. Both had, however, overlooked a crucial fact that infection was often enough conveyed in hospital and not at the moment of injury. At the same time, Wright never saw any reason to abandon the essentials of his case in the wisdom of after-experience. A post-script to the controversy appeared in *The Lancet* of June 15th, 1918. It was a paper which appeared under the names of Wright, Fleming and Colebrook, in which they reiterated the opinions they had always held as a result of their highly original experiments.

> "The treatment of bacterial infection," they stated, "is always approached with certain *a priori* assumptions. The surgeon who treats wounds with antiseptics assumes that the organism is unable to deal with the infecting microbes. The proper assumption would be that the organism must—for else there would be bacterial infections from which nobody could

recover—be competent to deal with every species of microbe. And clearly it is impossible to know what the body is capable of achieving, or to fix any limit to its bactericidal powers, before we have found out how to bring those powers effectively to bear, and before the conditions essential to success have been realised in wounds."

Having set out the course of their investigations, they headed their closing remarks : " What We Have To Unlearn," and they preface this final section with William James' penetrating observation : " We never fully grasp the import of any true statement until the opposite untrue statement is clearly set over against it."

However, the dusts of controversy were settling, and in the following year, after hostilities had ceased, Fleming was to review the arguments of both sides. With his uncommon faculty for synthesis, he was to show that there was a basis upon which they could be reconciled to each other.

CHAPTER VIII

SCEPTICISM AND ACTIVITY

THE WAR ended on November 11th, 1918. "The situation of Europe at the time of the Armistice," writes H. A. L. Fisher, " was one of unexampled misery and confusion. The vanquished Empires had crumbled to pieces and the new Republics had yet to acquire authority and confidence . . . Eight million young men, the best and most vigorous of their generation had been killed in the war. A greater number had been permanently disabled. Equally, if not more serious, were the losses consequent upon starvation, malnutrition, and disease . . . No words can paint the pangs and sufferings of this long-drawn agony of the European situation."

Fleming, at the age of thirty-seven, was demobilized from the Royal Army Medical Corps while holding the rank of Captain. But as he resumed his work in London, there lingered with him memories of the Boulogne days, some less forbidding than the muffled nocturne of uniformed men tramping through the shadowed streets, less haunting than the wordless resignation or the broken cries of the wounded and dying begging for relief. For to that fishing port, where in 1805 Napoleon had set up camp for an invasion of England, Wright and his group had transferred some of the memorable atmosphere of the pre-war days at St. Mary's when the talk after midnight turned to principles of morality, to philosophical questions, to shop and the Rabelaisian tale. Even its cosmopolitan character remained, for with them they had had Americans, Frenchmen, Belgians . . . They were still stimulated by a brew of tea, but their debates took place during the afternoon. There had even been the occasional round of golf when endless tasks permitted. At Boulogne also (so report went) the British Army had conspired with Dr. Harvey Cushing of the Harvard Medical Unit to employ Fleming's powers of persuasion and his sense of discretion in a sphere unrelated to microbes ; to him they gave the appointed task of seeing that Wright went out properly dressed—properly dressed, that is, in the view of the British Army. Dr. N. M. Keith of the Mayo Clinic in America has recollected those times :

" It was my good fortune when serving in the Royal Army Medical Corps during World War I to be invited to join the staff of the research laboratory in Boulogne. This unit was organized and directed by Sir Almroth Wright primarily for bacteriological research. It was there that I first met Sir Alexander Fleming. My job was to carry on a specific problem in clinical investigation for the army. Thus a stranger from America was cast among a group of superbacteriologists from England. It might have been a lonely life for me had not he (Fleming) been a most helpful counsellor and had we not become friendly rivals on the golf links at week-ends.

" A productive research unit has some individual characteristics. There were two that seem particularly evident in the Boulogne group. The first was that a frequent donation of a few drops of blood from a finger or ear to the bacteriological leeches was good policy. These samples of blood were used for controlled observations, so I learned that controls were fundamental in bacteriology as well as in chemical and physical research. But imagine my surprise, on requesting (Fleming) to donate 10cc. of his own venous blood, for chemical control of a new micromethod, that he hesitated and then only reluctantly gave me the necessary blood. He remarked as I put the sponge over the injured vein, ' I believe in England we have better bacteriologists, but you in America seem to lead in biochemistry '.

" The second characteristic of the laboratory was the type of discussion that would occur over the teacups during the afternoon recess. A recurring topic was the distinction between epistemic and pragmatic scientific discoveries. I slowly learned that the great discoveries of Newton and Einstein were epistemic, while the discovery of the prevention of enteric fever by inoculation of vaccine was pragmatic. . . ."

But behind the light curtain of distractions were the humane undertakings to which they addressed themselves, stirred by Wright's words that " all who follow the intellectually laborious calling of medicine should remember that God has given every mind the choice between truth and repose," shocked as true doctors by the immoderate waste of vital forces in war, quickened by times charged with grim urgency. " I was deeply impressed," Fleming has stated, " by the high mortality among wounded men who contracted infections in the First World War." So, sustained by his tenacity, by his will to reach the truth, he had gone into action, a master of his craft, mature of head and hands ; he had performed a series of beautiful experiments which were classics of the laboratory, and which proved to all but intractable minds that the prevailing methods of treating wound infections were unsound. And there had been intractable minds, rejecting the alternative of invoking the powers of Nature, thereby splitting the ranks of medicine.

"Science becomes dangerous," Shaw has written, " only when it imagines it has reached its goal. What is wrong with priests and popes is that instead of being apostles and saints, they are nothing but empirics who say ' I know ' instead of ' I am learning ' and pray for credulity and inertia as wise men pray for scepticism and activity." It is a comment appropriate to the division which had occurred, and appropriate also to Fleming's own case, for scepticism and activity had been to the forefront during his career, scepticism of an older order unassured by the trials of the laboratory, and activity in showing where it was at fault and in creating a new and scientifically assured order.

Now that the war was over he had a little breathing space in which to recall the endeavours of four intense years, the companionship of friends who had shared both work and recreation abroad, the enchantments of the laboratory and of imaginative, well-planned experiments adroitly conducted, the controversy springing from opposing ideas. His mind pivoted about the conviction to which he subscribed that " the treatment of bacterial infections is always approached with certain *a priori* assumptions," and he weighed in greater calm the implications of such matters in their translation from the special field of war-time medicine to civilian practice ; a goodly accumulation of experiences viewed with his insight and placed in proper design acquired the utmost relevance to his future. Invited to deliver the Hunterian Lecture before the Royal College of Surgeons in February 1919, he gave a masterly appraisal of " The Action of Chemical and Physiological Antiseptics in a Septic Wound ", considering with scrupulous care the dissensions caused by this vexing topic. He said :

"There have been during the war two schools in the treatment of wounds : the *physiological school*, which concentrated their efforts in aiding the natural protective agencies of the body against infection, and the *antiseptic* school, which aimed at killing the microbes in the wound with some chemical agent.

"Sir Almroth Wright and his followers have maintained that it is impossible for any of the commonly used antiseptics to have an appreciable effect in sterilizing a wound in which the infection has become established, and that the greatest benefit is to be obtained by aiding the physiological agencies which bring about the natural recovery from infection. . ."

What were the natural protective agencies of the body to which he referred ? They were, firstly, blood tissue and fluids, and, secondly, the leucocytes. Wright had shown that some of the bacteria commonly found in wounds grow very badly in unaltered blood serum, but that they will grow luxuriantly if its alkaline reaction is reduced or abolished. Into test tubes containing normal serum and the serum of a patient suffering from gas gangrene, he introduced graduated implantations of the bacillus of Welch. In the serum from the gas gangrene patient, which had lost almost all its alkalinity, growth took place with one-thousandth of the implantation necessary to induce growth in the normal serum ; moreover, the formation of gas was very much greater. As a result of this, alkali therapy was used as an adjunct to surgery with markedly good results in treating cases of severe gas-gangrene.

Again, Wright by experiment indicated that men suffering from severe septic infections had a greatly enhanced antitryptic power in their blood fluids, by antitryptic power meaning the capacity of the serum or lymph to neutralize tryptic ferments. Those microbes, which could grow in unaltered serum, he called ' serophytes '. Those others found in wounds he called ' sero-saprophytes ' since they grew badly in unaltered serum or lymph but flourish in such fluids when they have become ' corrupted '. As a result of toxic material produced by the bacteria in a wound, or the chemical substances introduced into it, some of the leucocytes disintegrate and in doing so liberate tryptic ferments, which diminish the antitryptic power of the lymph, or even render it tryptic, and so make it a good cultivation medium for all microbes generally found in a wound.

85

To keep up the antitryptic power of the wound discharge at a high level and to keep it free from corruption was therefore very necessary, in order to rid the wound of serosaprophytes. In practice it was found that the antitryptic content could not be maintained in the presence of sloughs. If the sloughs could not be excised by surgical means, they could be removed by the intermittent application of hypertonic salt solution, which broke up the leucocytes it met, liberated trypsin, and enabled the trypsin to act on the sloughs. With the application of the salt solution, fresh leucocytes emigrate into the cavity of the wound, to be destroyed with the next application of the hypertonic salt, a recurring process which ultimately clears the wound of sloughs.

Meanwhile, as a result of bacterial action, leucocytes break down and corrupt the lymph in the walls of the wound, where the really serious infection exists. It is therefore necessary to remove this corrupted lymph and replace it with fresh fluid possessed of its full antitryptic and antibacterial powers. Drainage of the tissues round the wound is just as important as the mechanical drainage of the cavity of the wound, and again the application of hypertonic salt solution causes a prompt flow of lymph from the tissues into the cavity of the wound.

Now it has long been known that the chief agents in the destruction of bacteria in a wound are the leucocytes. Wright devised methods proving their remarkable potency in this connection, which could first be shown with leucocytes obtained from the blood. Blood in itself contains too few leucocytes and too much fluid for the bactericidal action to be manifest, but there are ways of obtaining an aggregation of the leucocytes, so that they could then be brought to bear on microbes in large numbers, more or less comparable with the condition of things in a wound. Fleming describes Wright's dramatic experiment in this way :

" Blood is drawn from the finger into a narrow tube containing a small glass slip (which we have called a ' lath '), and the tube is centrifuged (shaken up) before the blood has time to clot. We then have the upper half of the tube filled with plasma and the lower with corpuscles. The leucocytes, being of slightly less specific gravity than the red corpuscles, are to a certain extent aggregated in the upper layers of the corpuscular portion. If we now place the tube in the incubator for an hour, the leucocytes emigrate on to the glass lath and adhere to it, and if this lath is taken out, washed free from red corpuscles and stained, it will be found that in the upper half, corresponding to the portion of the lath surrounded with plasma, there are no leucocytes. Towards the centre of the lath, corresponding with the upper corpuscular layer, there are an enormous number of leucocytes adhering to the lath, and these gradually diminish in numbers towards the bottom. If such a lath with the adherent leucocytes be placed on an infected agar plate, it will be found that the microbes are completely destroyed in the region where there are many leucocytes, while there is no inhibition of growth under the upper half of the lath on which there are no leucocytes. It was also found that leucocytes have the power of destroying the microbes even after they had been washed quite free from serum. In such a case no phagocytosis took place, yet there was a very definite direct bactericidal power exercised by the leucocytes.

"We see, then, that leucocytes collected from the blood are powerful bactericidal agents, and it now remains for us to see whether the leucocytes obtained from an infected wound behave in the same way."

He next describes his own experiments done to answer this question :

"Very soon after the infliction of a wound, leucocytes commence to collect in the walls and emigrate into the cavity of the wound, ultimately forming the cellular elements of pus. It used to be taught that pus was a collection of dead leucocytes but this only approaches accuracy when the pus is obtained from a collection which has stagnated and in which the leucocytes have been in contact with the bacteria for a considerable time. Some such pus was placed on an agar plate and covered over with a cover-slip, when the pus spread out in a thick film between the cover-slip and the agar. The plate was then incubated and innumerable (microbe) colonies developed throughout the pus, thus showing that the leucocytes had lost their bactericidal action.

"When fresh pus from an open wound was treated in the same way, no colonies developed in the pus, only a few colonies around the margin where some of the microbes had been squeezed out into the pus fluid and away from the reach of the pus cells by the weight of the cover slip. When the leucocytes are killed by heating them to 48°C. or by drying, many colonies develop, as when stale pus was used.

"We have shown that the cells of fresh pus can destroy the microbes contained in that pus, but they can do much more than this. If, instead of using a sterile agar plate, the pus is placed on an agar plate which has been heavily infected with staphylococcus or streptococcus, covered and incubated, it will be found that the pus has completely destroyed the added cocci in addition to destroying its own microbes."

This he named the technique of "bio-pyo culture", that is, of placing a small quantity of the pus on an agar plate and covering it with a cover-glass. He also employed a method he called the "impression culture", in which the culture is made by dropping a sterile cover-slip on the wound and immediately transferring it to an agar plate, and it served to confirm what he had already demonstrated : few bacterial colonies developed where the pus was adhering to the cover-slip but they did develop in the spaces between the islands of pus. It was by this method that he was able to show that after dressing a wound microbes could grow almost unhindered since most of the pus-cells had been washed away. Strikingly enough, specimens taken four hours and eight hours after the dressing remained sterile because there had been a fresh emigration of leucocytes capable of dealing with the infection.

Summarizing the treatment recommended by "the physiological school", based on the revelations of these and other experiments, he says :

"We have seen that in the early stages it is of prime importance to clean the wound of sloughs and to drain the tissues in addition to draining the cavity of the wound. In a later stage, we have seen that we must make such conditions that the leucocytes can exert their maximum effect on the bacteria. We can, however, by the administration of vaccines in appropriate doses, assist the local defences by raising the anti-bacterial content of the blood fluids. . . All vaccine treatment must, however, be secondary to proper local treatment of the wound."

It remained for him to deal with the claims of "the antiseptic school" :

"The teaching of the antiseptic school is that one should aim at the sterilization of the wound with a single application of the antiseptic ; failing this it is held that the antiseptic, even if it does not completely sterilize the wound, will kill a large number of the microbes present, so that it will at least diminish the amount of the infection, and will leave a medium in the cavity of the wound in which the microbes will not flourish. It is further held that, provided the antiseptic is used in dilute solution, no damage will be done. We shall see how these teachings bear the light of experiment.

" I shall have nothing to say regarding the action of these antiseptics on bacteria in a watery medium, as this has no bearing on their bactericidal action in an infected wound. Speaking generally, it has been found that antiseptic solutions show their maximum bactericidal action when they are allowed to act on the microbes in a watery medium, their action is more feeble when the medium is of a serous character ; it is still less in blood ; it is further reduced when the medium is of a purulent nature ; while least of all will an antiseptic act on bacteria embedded in a piece of tissue.

By a series of tests made to judge the inhibitory power of the common antiseptics on the growth of bacteria in serum, to judge the concentrations necessary to kill bacteria in pus, and to judge the strengths of antiseptics which inhibit leucocytic emigration and destroy the phagocytic power of the leucocytes, he demonstrated that no antiseptic was capable of sterilizing by a single application a wound in which the infection had become established. Indeed, the leucocytes, he found, are more sensitive to the action of the chemical antiseptic than are the bacteria, so that " it is unlikely that any of these antiseptics have the power of penetrating into the tissues and destroying the bacteria without first killing the tissues themselves." A most ingenious experiment illustrated well the impossibility of sterilizing with antiseptics a wound such as a projectile wound with its countless indentations. He describes it thus :

" I have attempted to imitate a wound in which the infection is limited to the cavity, by means of a tube which has several small processes drawn out to represent the diverticula which exist in all serious recently-inflicted gun-shot wounds. Into such a tube is placed some serum which has been implanted with faeces, and which makes a fair imitation of the primary infection of a wound. After this had been incubated so that the infection might spread throughout the whole tube, I tried to sterilize it with some of the antiseptics in common use. The procedure adopted was to pour out the contents and wash the tube three or four times with the antiseptic solution by filling the tube with it and emptying it out again. Then the tube was filled with the antiseptic solution and left for twenty minutes after which the antiseptic was poured out and replaced by serum. The tube was then incubated for twenty-four hours. The result was that there was no change in the flora of the tube on the second day. The next day I ' dressed ' it in the same way, but left the antiseptic in the tube for one hour. This had no effect. The next day the antiseptic was left in the tube for three hours, but it likewise had no effect. Then the antiseptic was allowed to remain in the tube for twenty-four hours, after which it was emptied out, replaced by serum and the tube incubated as before. Films were made of the contents of the tube and from the microscopic appearance of these films it will be seen that there is practically no difference between the tube dressed with normal saline and those in which the antiseptic solutions were used. This would seem to indicate clearly that it is impossible to sterilize a wound with an antiseptic even if it were possible to keep the antiseptic solution in the wound for a long time without dilution, and even if the walls of the wound were not infected.

" I tried to imitate the infected walls of the wound by placing a ball of infected asbestos wool, about the size of a pea, in a test tube, and I then attempted to sterilize it by filling the tube with Dakin's solution, which was changed at intervals during twenty-four hours. Then the Dakin's fluid was emptied out and the tube filled with serum and incubated. The tube which had been treated with Dakin's solution gave as good a growth as the control tube which had been treated with normal salt solution, and, on examining the growth under the microscope, there was found to be no change in the original flora."

He next asked the question : even if it does not completely sterilize a wound, does the antiseptic at least kill some of the microbes and so reduce the active infection in the wound ? He showed both by the bio-pyo culture and the impression-culture techniques, that, after washing, far from there being any diminution in the number of microbe colonies, there was an increase, because the natural antiseptic powers of the pus are done away with, and that microbes survive and thrive until fresh pus cells emigrate to check their growth.

A now classical experiment enabled him to answer yet another crucial question : antiseptics can do harm since they destroy leucocytes in forms less concentrated than required to kill microbes, but do these chemicals stimulate the growth of these microbes in serum ? In his own words :

" . . . we have used as a medium serum to which has been added trypsin sufficient to neutralize the anti-tryptic power of the serum or actually to render it tryptic. This is an imitation of the condition of things found in pus fluids. The serum was implanted with microbes, and then the antiseptic was added in various dilutions. Usually we have taken microbes which produced gas from serum, as these rendered the experiment easier in that the amount of gas produced gave an indication of the amount of growth of the microbe. The experiments were carried out in small test tubes, and, as soon as the mixtures were made, melted vaseline was poured on top of the fluid in the tube and allowed to set. The gas, as it was produced by the growth of the microbe, pushed up the vaseline plug so that the total amount of gas produced could readily be measured. 0.5 per cent. carbolic acid completely inhibited the growth of the bacillus of Welch in serum, but there is a regular rise in the amount of gas formation up to a maximum in the tube containing 0.06 per cent. carbolic acid, after which the amount of gas formed is less ; but even in the tube containing 0.015 per cent. there is rather more gas formation than in the control tube which contained no carbolic acid. . ."

After other experiments with different antiseptics, he concluded :

It is not possible to sterilize a septic wound with a single application of any of the commonly used antiseptics.

Although, doubtless, the antiseptic kills some microbes in the cavity of the wound, it also inhibits the leucocytes so that the active residual infection may actually be increased.

The antiseptic does not, of necessity, leave in the wound a medium which is inhibitory to the growth of microbes ; on the contrary, it may have a stimulating effect on their growth.

In a final appreciation, he not only found a point of synthesis between two schools of thought but enunciated a permanent guiding principle, for so far all known antiseptics damaged the body cells. The problem before science, therefore, was to discover an antiseptic inocuous in this respect. He said : " I venture to suggest that the antiseptics at present in use will only exercise a beneficial effect in a septic wound if they possess the property of stimulating or conserving the natural defensive mechanism of the body against infection. If such a thesis be true, then it brings the 'antiseptic' and 'physiological' treatments on to the same basis, and it also makes it necessary, in the estimation of the value of an antiseptic, to study its effect on the tissues more than its effect on the bacteria."

Antiseptics, he maintained, find their true application in preventing the infection of war wounds, in their prophylactic treatment; they should be lavishly used outside the wound, there should be early and thorough surgical treatment and careful dressing. Experiment showed that chemical agents as adjuncts to surgery had doubtful value. And there is a sardonic flicker in his admonition of surgeons: "If this is so, then there is a very great disadvantage in the use of an antiseptic from the surgeon's point of view. It is very difficult for the surgeon not to be deluded into the belief that he has in the antiseptic a second string to his bow, and consequently it will tend to make him less careful in his surgical treatment of the wound. If he knows that he has nothing to fall back on, then, even with the most conscientious individuals, the surgery would improve. Because of this alone it would be well if the treatment of the *wound* with antiseptics in the early stage were abandoned and the surgeon relied on his skill alone. All the great successes of primary wound treatment have been due to efficient surgery, and it seems a pity that the surgeon should wish to share his glory with a chemical antiseptic of more than doubtful utility."

These triumphant accomplishments (modestly recognized when he was mentioned in despatches) he had quietly recounted to his distinguished professional hearers that winter evening in 1919. They could hardly have missed the fine sense of justice which had enabled him so fairly to present two sides of the case—even though he had a foot in the dissidents' camp—the scope of his technical ingenuity and his productivity, and all must have been conscious of the sense of authority springing from him. They saw him, to use again Professor Pannett's words, "reticent, dour, acutely perceptive, more aware than anybody else that antiseptics were quite hopeless as therapeutic applications." Yet he himself dismisses this first climax towards which his career had mounted in two sentences: "During the last war I went to France with my chief, Sir Almroth Wright, and we settled down to study septic wounds and the action of antiseptics. Ever since then I have been partial to the study of antiseptics."

In this partiality to the study of antiseptics, perhaps, are the first faint signs of stir and preparation for future events. Apart from the forceful impression made upon him by Ehrlich's Salvarsan, a chemotherapeutic remedy, he had concerned himself chiefly with the body's natural defences. " I learned early in my medical career the real value of natural antiseptics." And again : " Experiments I (and others) made convinced me that probably the most important antibacterial agents in the body are the cells themselves."

And Nature was soon to recompense him for his close study of her, going back to boyhood days, by revealing to him the presence of one of her most extraordinary creations, made for the protection of the human organism.

CHAPTER IX

THE PRECURSOR OF PENICILLIN

THE INFLUENZA pandemic which followed the war and produced such extremities of suffering was to medicine a baffling phenomenon, no doubt connected with the privations and nervous exhaustions which the populations of the world endured during hostilities and in a chaotic aftermath. Naturally Fleming engaged in a study of the disease. In particular he considered the problems of growing the so-called influenza bacillus on various culture media, since the traditional text-book methods produced only pin-point colonies of the germ which were difficult to see with the naked eye. At St. Mary's they had used different methods which induced good growth but were cumbersome and time-taking in preparation. He showed by neat, convincing experiments that the bacillus could be made to thrive on media much more simply and expeditiously made ready ; he showed also that by the addition of a chemical antiseptic, brilliant green, to the medium, the development of other cocci could be much restricted, thereby leaving the influenza germs almost isolated and easy to investigate. Moreover, he suggested a means by which cultures of the influenza bacillus could be kept alive for a considerable time since it was often hard to prevent them from dying too quickly.

He was then joined by Lt. Col. Francis J. Clemenger of the American Army Medical Corps in carrying these researches further. The German scientist, Pfeiffer, had described this bacillus as the cause of the influenza epidemic of 1890–91, but until the pandemic after the First World War there had been little opportunity of confirming his theory. Indeed, the bacteriological evidence had served to cast doubts on Pfeiffer's supposition, and the question that Fleming and Clemenger tried to answer turned on whether Pfeiffer's bacillus was the primary infective agent, or a secondary invader along with other organisms like the pneumococcus and the streptococcus, which ordinarily caused inflammations in the respiratory tract

Now it had been found impossible to induce an attack of influenza by spraying the throat with a pure culture of the bacillus. Furthermore, before the epidemic, the bacillus was often to be found in catarrhal conditions of the respiratory tract, and especially in cases of chronic bronchitis. It thus seemed unlikely that an organism whose presence was so common when no epidemic prevailed should suddenly have caused a world-wide pandemic of influenza. It could be easily understood how such a bacillus on gaining access to a community which had previously had no dealings with it could set up a local epidemic, but it was difficult to understand how it could set one up so rapidly, spreading over the world and affecting communities in which it had been a common inhabitant of the human body. On the other hand, it was undeniably present in people suffering from influenza.

Strains of the Pfeiffer bacillus were obtained from Boulogne, Etaples and in London, and subjected to test. If all the strains could be shown to give the same immunity reactions, Fleming and Clemenger would have had evidence to support the idea that the infection spread from one person to another. If the immunity reactions were different, however, they would have to believe rather that the infective agent was of a different nature and that it excited invasion by the bacillus of Pfeiffer, which was perhaps leading a saprophytic existence in the respiratory tract.

Their experiments clearly indicated so much difference between the various strains that it was profitless to continue, and at about the same time they had news from a Dr. Park of New York that he too had been forced to similar conclusions, after testing reactions of the bacillus obtained from different members of a small community who had obviously been infected with influenza from a common source. The influenza bacillus of Pfeiffer was in fact an associated group of bacteria, and it seemed more than likely that it was not the leading cause of influenza, but that it was awakened into activity by a primary infective organism, residing in the respiratory tract. " The question whether or not an individual can be protected against an epidemic of influenza by means of a vaccine is one which is of the greatest importance in medical practice," they wrote, and the practical value of their findings was reflected in their recommendations that as many strains of the Pfeiffer bacillus should be incorporated in the vaccine given to patients so as to make it widely polyvalent.

But these enquiries into the origins of influenza were only a fraction of Fleming's activities during the years immediately after the war, divided between incessant work in the laboratories and his duties in the lecture room, for in 1919 he had been appointed Assistant Lecturer in Bacteriology at St. Mary's Hospital. Set in purpose, disciplined in conduct, ingenious yet patient, courageous yet cautious, he kept moving quietly forward, every lineament of personality more heavily defined by the hands of time and experience. It has been said that there can be no encounter with Eternal Verity in science, only encounters with greater and smaller truths, often fugitive and phantom-like but always as important to the scientist as a trodden leaf or a broken twig to a skilful tracker, or as the signs of weather to a shepherd. And suddenly as he advanced at his own steady pace along a road constantly dividing and branching off in perplexing directions and towards unknown destinations, the skies seemed to open and shed upon him a special radiance, for unexpectedly he met with one of the greater truths. " Fortune had not finished with me," he could say, " she continued to be kind, for a purely accidental happening in the laboratory led me to the discovery of a substance which had an extraordinary power of dissolving microbes, which I christened lysozyme."

But there is still Pasteur's dictum to restrain any over-hasty dismissal of such events with a few words about luck. " There are no accident in science," he had said. Others yet might well see in them the hand of God, some superior direction of human affairs. Dr. Wallace E. Herrell of the Mayo Clinic in America, when he welcomed Fleming there in February 1946, had certain comments to make about this subject : " I would like to say a word or two about serendipity," he remarked, " I have on occasions heard scientists defend the thesis that most important observations and discoveries were serendipitous in nature. I do not believe that scientific discoveries for the most part, are accidental, as sometimes they are declared to be. Scientific discoveries are the result of carefully planned and methodically executed procedures, made possible by days and weeks of controlled observations. It is certainly no accident that Sir Alexander Fleming has been deeply interested during his whole career in the destruction of bacteria by various agents, including leucocytes. This particular interest of his dates back to the time when he was a pupil of Sir Almroth Wright. It was no accident that during the war of 1914–18 he investigated problems in connection with septic wounds. It was no accident that in 1922 he described lysozyme, a potent anti-bacterial ferment . . . ''

It was on February 13th, 1922, that the Royal Society received through Sir Almroth Wright a paper by Fleming with the title : " On A Remarkable Bacteriolytic Element found in Tissues and Secretions. " In this communication," he wrote, " I wish to draw attention to a substance present in the tissues and secretions of the body, which is capable of rapidly dissolving certain bacteria. As this substance has properties akin to those of ferments I have called it 'Lysozyme' . . . ''

But behind these deceptively formal statements lives the strangely designed story of this discovery, its beginnings stemming from the overwhelming curiosity of Fleming's disposition. He was suffering from troublesome catarrh, so he started to investigate his own nasal secretions, which day by day he cultivated on blood agar plates. For the first three days of the infection he saw no microbial growth except for an occasional staphylococcus colony, but on the fourth day when he examined his culture he saw to his astonishment a large microbe which he could not exactly identify. When fully developed he noted that it was round, opaque, and of a bright yellow colour. He named it the *Micrococcus lysodeikticus*. As he continued with his experiments, he was again astonished to find that one drop of diluted nasal mucus added to a single cubic centimetre of a thick suspension of the cocci caused it to vanish from his sight in a few minutes.

Describing his feelings as he watched so unique a phenomenon he has said : " Lysozyme has a remarkable lytic action, a most extraordinary lytic action. I had been brought up to observe bacteriolysis by putting anti-serum in with microbes, putting the mixture into the water-bath and waiting some considerable time to see the lysis, which very often wasn't complete. But in working with this antibiotic substance, lysozyme, which is found especially strongly in human tears, we took a thick milky suspension of the right bacteria and added the smallest quantity of tears, and kept the mixture warm for just about thirty seconds. In that short time it became perfectly clear. I had never seen such rapid bacteriolysis."

Another experiment, as strikingly dramatic, added proof of the amazing inhibitory powers of lysozyme. In his own words:

" A small portion of the agar is removed from an ordinary agar plate making a cup into which some material rich in lysozyme (tears, nasal mucus, sputum, cartilege, egg-white, etc.) is placed. A drop of liquid agar at a temperature of about 50°C is placed on the material in the cup and is allowed to solidify, after which the cup is filled with the liquid agar which, in its turn, is allowed to set. Liquid agar is then poured all over the plate to make a thin layer over the original surface. The whole surface of the medium is now thickly planted with the *Micrococcus lysodeikticus* and the plate is incubated for twenty-four hours, when it will be seen that there is copious growth of the coccus, except in the region of the implanted material. By the method of preparation of the plate, in which the material is covered with several distinct layers of agar, there can be no mechanical transference of the material to the surface of the plate, but the experiment shows that the inhibitory substance is able to penetrate the agar and absolutely prevent growth of the coccus for a distance of about one centimetre. Further, if the plate is kept for a few days, it is found that portions of the growth next to the inhibition zone have become almost transparent, and it is evident that the lytic substance has continued to diffuse through the agar after the microbes have completed their growth, and has dissolved the cocci for a distance of three or four m.m."

To ascertain the bactericidal power of lysozyme, Fleming made cultures from the inhibition zone of his agar plate. There was no growth, the bacteria implanted on this surface had been destroyed. When he incubated a faecal streptococcus with tears diluted one hundred times and with normal saline solution, a continuous sheet of growth resulted in the saline tube, whereas in the tube containing the tears were a few sporadic colonies of the microbe ; most of the streptococci had been destroyed. Lysozyme was later used on a small scale at St. Mary's Hospital for the dissolution of faecal streptococci in the intestine, and in Soviet Russia it came to be used more extensively in various conditions.

Apart from nasal mucus, tears and sputum, a very large number of tissues and organs of the body were discovered to be the repositories of this natural antiseptic. To investigate the lysozyme-content of the tissues, small portions of them no larger than a split-pea were placed in tubes containing 1cc of a thick suspension of the *Micrococcus lysodeikticus*. They were then incubated at a temperature of 45°C and if the suspensions lost their opaque look, it was evidently because of lytic action. Some of those tissues were obtained from the post-mortem room, others from laboratory workers or from the operating theatre. It turned out that practically all the tissues and organs possessed some lytic power, even a few hairs from the head caused a solution of these cocci.

It is also present in great concentration in the leucocytes, and to demonstrate this, Fleming placed two glass rings on a slide, filling one of them with blood and incubating it for an hour to allow the leucocytes to emigrate to the surface of the slide. He next threw off the blood-clot, and washed the leucocytes adhering to the surface of the slide free of red corpuscles and serum, after which he filled both cells with a strong suspension of M. Lysodeikticus. After an hour in the incubator the cocci in the cell with a carpet of leucocytes had all been dissolved, whereas in the control cell without leucocytes there was no solution of the cocci.

Plasma and serum also contain lysozyme, and it exists in fairly large amounts in the fibrin (coagulable lymph) of the blood clot. " It is conceivable," wrote Fleming, " that this is a protective mechanism for open wounds, which rapidly become covered with a layer of fibrin and leucocytes, both of which are rich in lysozyme."

Joined in his researches by a colleague, Dr. V. D. Allison, the two of them pressed their enquiries outside the purely human domain. The hen's egg forms one of the staple articles of man's diet. As it is marketed it does not reach the consumer until many days after it is laid, but if eggs from a shop window are examined bacteriologically it is found that, as a rule, they are sterile. Now the contents of the egg are highly albuminous, and both white and yolk can be used in the laboratory, after treatment in various ways, as culture media for bacteria. It is thus clear that ample foodstuff exists in the egg for the development of microbes, but yet, in the ordinary course of events, bacteria do not invade the egg for a long time after it is laid and exposed to infection.

By what means is it protected from infection then? By the shell? Experiments show that many bacteria can quite readily pass through the shell, although the infection of the egg's contents is delayed mechanically. Some scientists had shown that egg-white had antibacterial properties, but they did not demonstrate the vast potency of its antibacterial action, nor did they connect this with similar powers existing in the tissues and secretions of humans and other animals. Fleming and Allison proved that the bacteriolytic power of egg-white was due to its high lysozyme content, which it possessed in common with many other living substances and their products. Indeed, clinically they recommended a number of patients who had a large number of streptococci in their faeces to take egg-white. In most cases they reported a definite temporary relief from the feelings of lassitude and headache which so often accompany an excess of these microbes in the intestine. If their relief was not permanent, it was probably because the microbes grew resistant to the lytic action of the egg-white, and could after a time flourish in the small amount of lysozyme that found its way into the intestine.

Next they found that egg-white from different species of birds like the moorhen, the wagtail and the thrush were all capable of inhibiting bacterial growth, while Fleming himself hooked a pike, spread its eggs out over a plate in the shape of the letter P, and showed that it too had this way of inhibiting bacteria. When egg-white was injected into a rabbit, the animal's serum showed marked antibacterial qualities over several hours, and there was no damage done to the leucocytes.

Extending their enquiry into the vegetable kingdom, Fleming and Allison tried to detect lysozyme in a large number of roots and tubers, but of them only the turnip showed any marked bacteriolytic effect. They also found lysozyme in various parts of the cut flower, having examined tulips, sunflowers, carnations, lupin, buttercup, elder, dock, nettle, poppy, candytuft and syringa among others. It occurred too in human milk, with marked influence on the bacterial inhabitants of the infant's intestine. Afterwards two German scientists showed that, with breast-fed children, it could be detected in their stools the third day after their birth, while in " artificially fed " children, it could not be found. " This is a feature of lysozyme which has not heretofore been noted," writes Fleming, " it may be an important one in the welfare of infants." He himself examined cow's milk, and found that four Jerseys had more lysozyme in their milk than the other animals under test, though none of the milk samples contained it in high degree. And one more curious fact, to indicate that dog saliva is, perhaps, more active than that of humans : when a carious human tooth is implanted in a dog's mouth the infected dentine is sterilized in a comparatively short time.

In testing the inhibitory effect on bacteria of material containing lysozyme, Fleming used two techniques in particular, and the extreme skill he reached in their application were in time to serve great purposes. " It was fortunate," he has said, " that much of the technique used for lysozyme was again employed in investigating penicillin." Also : " In the study of lysozyme methods were devised which proved extremely useful when penicillin came on the scene." One of these techniques was the slide-cell, which Wright had devised for investigating the bactericidal power of the whole blood, but which Fleming had deftly adapted to a variety of uses, and which he has called, " a contraption I'm rather fond of." For the other, he took an agar plate and with a knife cut a strip out of it. In the resulting gutter he put material containing lysozyme, and he then planted microbes in streaks at right angles to it. Some microbes grew right up to the gutter, others stopped some way short of it, and he determined the sensitivity of the organism to lysozyme by the distance between the gutter and the point at which the microbe began its growth.

Moreover, he was convinced that the skin contains lysozyme, and that this was not confined to the deeper layers of the skin. He has stated :

"If a suspension is made of a susceptible organism like M. *lysodeikticus* and to it is added some scrapings from the surface of the skin, the paring of a corn, or even a small cutting of a finger nail, it will be found that after, say, one hour's incubation the opaque suspension will be completely cleared.

"It is my custom when dealing with bacteriolysis in our classes to provide for the students a suspension of M. *lysodeikticus* and get them to whittle off a portion of a finger nail and drop it into the suspension. When they find that after about an hour the bacteria have completely disappeared they are very much impressed, especially as they have recently come from the hands of the physiologist who has taught them that the finger nails consist of inert tissue.

"But it is quite obvious that the superficial layers of the skin must have some mechanism for destroying bacteria. We are continually soiling our hands and fingers with many bacteria —most of us are not above putting a finger into our mouths on occasion, but how often can one obtain a mouth organism from scrapings from the finger? We have already seen that extracts of skin have a considerable lytic effect on some pathogenic bacteria.

"Observations on the anti-bacterial powers of the cutis have been made by Colebrook here, and by Lloyd Arnold and others in America. They found that large numbers of pathogenic bacteria (including haemolytic streptococci from puerperal septicaemia) which were placed on the skin, disappeared. That is, they could not be recovered in cultures made by washing the skin in a culture medium. This may be lysozyme action. So far there is no proof. . ."

Yet after all this exhaustive work, extending over years, and all the creative flair he had displayed in searching out the capacities and functions of an unknown natural antiseptic, a certain text-book on bacteriology off-handedly referred to it in this fashion : "Lysozyme, described by Fleming in various secretions, especially tears, and in tissues, causes rapid solution of some saprophytic cocci." Understandably he came back with a rebuttal of so inadequate an account, enumerating carefully its outstanding features, all verified by evidence gathered in his laboratory :

That lysozyme is a widely distributed antibacterial ferment which is probably inherent in all animal cells and constitutes a primary method of destroying bacteria.

That lysozyme, while acting most strikingly on non-pathogenic bacteria, yet can, when allowed to act in the full strength in which it occurs in some parts of the body, attack pathogenic organisms.

That it is very easy to make bacteria relatively resistant to lysozyme, so that any pathogenic microbe isolated from the body where it has been growing in the presence of a non-lethal concentration of lysozyme, must have acquired increased resistance to the ferment.

That there are some differences in the lysozyme of different tissues and in different animals whereby bacteria are susceptible to different lysozymes in varying degrees.

Later he gave this definition of lysozyme :

' It is a bacteriolytic ferment which acts on the carbohydrate moiety of certain bacteria and causes their rapid dissolution."

Delivering the President's Address to the Royal Society of Medicine in December, 1932, Fleming opened by saying : " I choose lysozyme as the subject for this address for two reasons, firstly because I have a fatherly interest in the name, and secondly because its importance in connection with natural immunity does not seem to be generally appreciated. . . . My contribution to the subject—apart from the name—has been an elucidation of the properties of the lytic element, a description of its wide distribution in Nature, and some estimate of its importance in immunity."

Natural immunity ! Here he was returning to a subject very close to his heart. He had emphasised it repeatedly during his professional life ; indeed, it ran like a *leit motif*, through his career, formulated during his protracted labours on phagocytosis and borne to its first climax by the end of the war when he had so thoroughly studied antiseptics and wound infections. " . . . I could never forget the importance of the body's natural defences ! " He now dwells on it again in talking of lysozyme, contrasting its ideal properties with the shortcomings of chemicals :

" When we contrast in our minds the powers of the natural ' antiseptics ' of the body with the chemical antiseptics, we are all probably inclined to believe that the former are weak in comparison. Possibly this is because in the past the testing of chemical antiseptics has for the most part been done under conditions which are very favourable to the antiseptic, while the testing of the bactericidal agents normally present in the body has perforce often to be done under conditions unfavourable to them. In the following experiment the natural antiseptic lysozyme, is compared with the common chemical antiseptics in use, under conditions not unfavourable to the former.

" Small discs are cut out of an agar culture plate with a cork borer, and in the cavities so produced discs of filtre paper soaked in natural or chemical antiseptics are placed. The cavities are then filled in with melted agar and the whole surface is planted thickly with bacteria. The natural antiseptics chosen are tears and nasal mucus, both of which are high in lysozyme, and the microbe chosen is *M. lysodeikticus* which, while it presents about the usual resistance to the chemical antiseptics, is specially susceptible to lysozyme action. There is no growth of the coccus near the embedded tears and nasal mucus, while there is a thick sheet of growth over all the chemical antiseptics—namely, iodine, 1 in 100 ; carbolic acid, 1 in 20 ; mercuric chloride, 1 in 1000 ; flavine, 1 in 1000 ; brilliant green, 1 in 500 ; gentian violet, 1 in 100 ; and mercurochrome, 1 in 100. Such an experiment shows that, given favourable conditions, the natural antiseptics have a far greater antibacterial effect than the commonly used chemical antiseptics in the strengths in which they are employed."

And once more he takes up his case :

" When one uses chemical antiseptics, it is well to consider whether the chemical will interfere with lysozyme action. In fact, most of the older chemical antiseptics completely stop lysozyme action in concentrations less than are necessary to inhibit bacterial growth. The following is a very instructive experiment :
" An agar culture plate is thickly inoculated with *M. lysodeikticus* (a microbe very susceptible to lysozyme). Three discs are punched out of the plate, and into the cups so formed are placed saliva in the first, Eusol in the third, and in the middle one a mixture of Eusol and saliva. After incubation the saliva inhibits bacterial growth for a considerable distance, Eusol also inhibits to some extent the growth of this organism, but the mixture is without effect. The hypochlorite destroys the lysozyme of the saliva, and the proteins of the saliva break up the hypochlorite. This is merely one instance of a chemical antiseptic interfering with the natural protective mechanism."

Thus the chemical antiseptic not only damages the leuco-cytes, it also vitiates the proper function of lysozyme, and the body is denied the fullest advantages of two of its chief protective devices. Finally he says :

" It seems hardly likely that the human body should have been endowed with such a powerful antibacterial force unless it were of use. The wide distribution of lysozyme in the cells of the tissues and organs rather suggests that this antibacterial agency is one of the primal protections of the cell against bacterial invasion, while its greatest concentration in certain tissues and secretions indicates that its elaboration or secretion has become specially enhanced in certain regions which are particularly exposed to infection or which are lacking in other means of protection.

" The eye, the nose, and the lower respiratory tract are constantly exposed to those organisms commonly met with in the air, and it is towards these organisms that the lysozyme of tears, nasal mucus and sputum are most powerful. There could be no chance of a microbe such as the *M. lysodeikticus* invading the body, as it would be killed and dissolved by the secretions long before it could proliferate and set up an infection.

" The use for an efficient bacterial agency in cartilege (rich in lysozyme) is clear, as this tissue is practically without blood supply, so that if microbes did gain access the bactericidal powers of the blood, which might prove effective in other tissues would here be without avail. . .

" The view has been very generally held that the function of tears, saliva, sputum, etc. in relation to infections was to rid the body of microbes by washing them away. Metchnikov, in his treatise on ' Immunity and Infectious Disease ', expresses himself very clearly and precisely on this point :

" ' Nature to protect the skin and mucuous membranes does not use antiseptics. The fluids which bathe the surface of the mouth and other mucus membranes are not bactericidal or very imperfectly so. Nature removes from the mucus mem-branes and the skin quantities of microbes, eliminating them by epithelial desquamation and expelling them with the secre-tions and liquid excretions. Nature has chosen this mechanical procedure just as the surgeons who replace the antisepsis of the mouth, the intestines, and other organs by lavage with physiological saline.'

" Such a view must be profoundly modified, and the direct bactericidal action of the tissues and secretions must be con-sidered an important factor in natural immunity."

Fleming had thus come upon a mysterious substance, all-pervasive in the human body and in Nature. It is probable that a good many airborne bacteria which are non-pathogenic are prevented from ever becoming pathogenic because human secretions display such destructive power towards them. Yet after he had done such brilliantly original work and evolved ingenious techniques to bring it to fulfilment, a last vital question remained : in what manner could lysozyme be placed at the disposal of the sick ? He supplies the answer himself : " It was unfortunate that from the purely medical point of view the microbes which were most strongly inhibited were those which were not pathogenic (i.e. those which do not cause disease) to men, so lysozyme has not taken an important place in therapeutics, although when concentrated it is not without action on many of the common pathogenic ones."

It seemed at the time tragically disappointing, for though discovery is its own reward and each new discovery a peak from which the scientist may survey his world of to-morrow, the greatest joy it can give is when he knows he has added something practical to the means of relieving physical distress. As he has himself recorded : " In my own work the greatest pleasure of the research men is a discovery however small. But it is just the same with a shepherd. If he has a chance of alleviating the sufferings of one of his flock, well, he gets the same pleasure."

Fleming had published his findings, and though they commanded the interest of specialists, including Professor Jules Bordet of the Pasteur Institute in Paris, who was to become his friend, by and large they fell on the unreceptive ears of medical men, chiefly because lysozyme had small practical applications. At this disconsolate moment if some-body had existed with the power of divination, if somebody could then have been set magically at a more advanced moment in time so as to acquire hind-sight, the discovery of lysozyme could have been viewed as we view it now : the essential precursor of an untold benefit to humanity. Meanwhile, the Fates had spun their mosaic with its baffling, unfinished spaces, leaving no portent that they intended to finish it in their own good time.

Professor Charles Pannett gives this version of these events :

" Here was Fleming, reticent, dour, acutely perceptive, more aware than anybody that antiseptics were quite hopeless as therapeutic applications. Yet he was the agent selected by Providence to discover the most wonderful of all antiseptics and at the same time open up a new field of investigation all over the world.

" For the great discovery (of penicillin), Fleming was prepared in a very curious and interesting fashion. He was first afflicted with a cold, and being of an inquisitive disposition, he proceeded to culture some of his nasal secretion and found to his astonishment that it contained a substance inhibitory to bacterial growth and he traced this substance to his tears. Where they dropped on a culture plate clear spaces remained. He called the active substance lysozyme. Hitherto all known antiseptics had injured tissue cells more than bacteria. Here was one which was harmless to cells.

" The first stage in the discovery of penicillin had been accomplished.

" It was with a mind prepared in this way, and used to seeing hiatuses in bacterial cultures that he gazed upon that fateful Petri dish, contaminated with the unknown mould."

And by one of those recurring concatenations of an unpredictable destiny, it is now a matter of history that in 1929 Howard Florey, who with his team, was afterwards to realise the full therapeutic values of penicillin, commenced work on lysozyme. He and his co-workers purified the enzyme and characterised its substrate.

CHAPTER X

THE NATURAL DEFENCES OF THE BODY

WHEN FLEMING discovered lysozyme in 1922, he was forty-one years old. In the previous year he had married Sarah Marion McElroy, daughter of John McElroy of Leigherntain House, Killala, County Mayo in Ireland. She was the twin-sister of his brother John's wife, and, like the Fleming family, the two sisters had left their native country to come and live in London. Temperamentally he and his wife were interestingly contrasted, since she was as gay and volatile as he was reserved and quiet, but in the attraction of opposites, perhaps, they were well suited to each other. It was the beginning of a happy marriage.

Meanwhile, biologists and bacteriologists all over the world had come to hear of his publications on lysozyme, and the titles of the papers written about it both by British and foreign scientists duly covered four type-written sheets of quarto paper. Soviet scientists took a particular interest in it. Yet neither this nor the other illuminating discoveries he had made possessed the assets of the hyper-dramatic which would carry them out of the serene unconcern of the bacteriological laboratory, out of the academic columns of medical journals with limited circulations to the ears of the editors of great national newspapers, avid for a sensation to drop among their millions of readers. " With great merit and even greater modesty," Montaigne has written, "one can remain unknown a long time."

Great merit he owned. And great modesty, which in later, renowned days was a quality that shone out. When he was a guest of honour at the Mayo Clinic in America in July 1946, his friend of the Boulogne days, Dr. Keith, in reminiscing about their tea-time discussions, turning upon the distinction between epistemic and pragmatic discoveries, wanted to know whether he would inform them into which of the two categories he would place his own far-reaching discovery of penicillin. And the answer he received from Fleming was : " Dr. Keith has asked me if the discovery of penicillin was pragmatic or epistemic. I don't know, but, you see, I am not a scholar, just a bacteriologist, that's all. I am one of the fortunate bacteriologists who happens to have done something which came into medical practice. Most bacteriologists do far better things but they are just plain bacteriologists and the physicians don't use them. But what I did came into medical practice and the result is—well, it is very difficult for a bacteriologist to cope with the situation."

The truth was that the large public cared little about the tranquil delights of laboratories, about subtle deductions from beautiful and dramatic experiments, about natural philosophy which science is. Its appetite in an increasingly technological age was for discoveries bearing relationship to an improvement in its own welfare, an appetite since considerably sharpened by the achievements of science during and after the Second World War. Sir Edward Appleton has had some pungent observations to make concerning its indifference to theoretical inspiration and to the creative processes occurring in the minds of the men who have delivered their gifts to society ; concerning its craving for the commodities of science alone, which the purveyors may seize upon and bring to the market-places. He condemned the view that there are superior and inferior forms of scientific activity according to whether there is or is not a practical human end in sight. " I want to break down the distinction," he said, " between what is called pure and applied research, believing they are essentially one . . . The public has become so accustomed to the enjoyment of the fruits of science that there is a great danger lest they should regard the scientist as a servant whose set task is to produce a succession of scientific discoveries of immediate use to industry or directly to the community."

Thus, midway through his life Fleming stood, by common consent distinguished in his profession, recognized by all behind the closed doors of the world of science, among the initiates familiar with its terms and its rituals. His youthful days had been spent in the expiring decades of materialist philosophy when the universe was explained as a vast machine, with matter "something lying out there in space; hard, simple, obvious, indubitably real, and as such calculated to form an admirable foundation upon which the horse-sense of the practical man would base his irrefragable conclusions." There were Newton's three laws; the pronouncements of Huxley, who was Darwin's interpreter, and of Haeckel; there was the conservation of energy; evil was visibly disappearing from the world; the atom was indivisible, the periodic law of no special note; things happened because of a few simple rules. As the present century moved on, however, the intellectual climate changed; the blue skies of certainty became flecked with the grey of doubt, and matter (using Prof. Joad's simile) became more and more "like the grin on the face of the Cheshire cat. Only the animal itself was fading and fading while the grin was growing bigger and bigger with less and less to sustain it."

Earlier complacency was, however, broken decisively in the medical circles to which Fleming belonged and from which he took his colour, for Wright had come with his penetrating intellect and having forced open the treasure-chest of medical knowledge pronounced it bare save for a valuable piece or two. With the help of Fleming and others he set out to enrich it. He had preached a challenging cause towards which Fleming had been drawn. Eagerly he had breathed in the free airs of Wright's laboratory at St. Mary's, revelling in its tingling atmosphere. "As Dean of St. Mary's Medical School," Lord Moran has said, " I have seen inspectors come round smiling approval. Until they reach the pathological department. The intellectual freedom of Sir Almroth Wright had alienated official favour." Fleming was happy in the liberty of expression and of action he met there, for he always had an opinion of his own from which he was not easily shifted, and an acute sense of his individuality. " It is the individual human, working out his own design of life who gives the world what progress it has made." He could not better have epitomized his consciousness of that individuality.

True genius, according to Dr. Johnson, is a mind of large general powers, accidentally determined to some particular

direction, ready for all things, but chosen by circumstances for
one. So recalls Dr. René J. Dubos in his fine study of Pasteur,
and goes on to say :

"Although the existence of these multiple potentialities, only
a few of which find expression during the life of any individual,
is most obvious and overpowering in the case of outstanding
creators, it is not peculiar to genius. It is characteristic of all
men, indeed of all living things, and Pasteur had even encountered it in the microbial world . . . there exists for each
one of us the potentiality of revealing ourselves to the world as
many different individuals, but circumstances allow us to live
only one of the many lives we could have lived. It is often by
a trivial, even an accidental decision that we direct our activities into a certain channel . . . "

Fleming might have been a good farmer, he might have
become a name in shipping, but his brother, Thomas, had
" pushed " him into medicine, and he had found his niche.
" One of the chief reasons for discontent," he has observed,
" is that people do not find the right niche in the world. It is
surprising just how many people do find the right place for
themselves. If a boy's people have too much money, he has
not the incentive, the need to spur him on. The poor boy has
to earn his living too soon." Fortune had in the nick of time
taken him out of his City job and enabled him to go into
medicine and in it find contentment. And success.

But he has always had his misgivings about success. What
was success ? He wondered if achieving ambition was success.
Yet ambition, thriving upon success, grew and never stopped.
" Was Robert Burns, Ayrshire's national poet, a success ? "
he has asked. " How many business men would like, at the
end of their lives to be engaged as an exciseman at twenty-
seven shillings a week ? Yet Burns was a genius, a success as
a poet." As for success in medicine, these misgivings were
appeased by the reflection that it did not mean " harming
other people. Success in medicine was more or less pure gain
to the community." There were the flowers of life, but there
was also the toil of cultivating them ; there were obstacles to
be overcome by patience in the conception of any worthy task,
by working at the difficulties which arose in its execution.

There might be luck, but luck alone was not enough ; nothing could be taken for granted, least of all the power within, hinting at roads to greatness. " You have to work and work to become skilful masters of your craft and think about your work and understand what you are doing. One most important thing —you have got to be honest not only towards others but towards yourselves, because it is only then that you can do your best." He abhors untidy, poorly-planned activity ; work and mastery of craft : they are his inviolable ideals, they are the two things he unfailingly commends in others. Speaking of Pasteur, he has said : " Louis Pasteur in his youth and throughout his life believed in hard work. He lived for his work and put his whole heart and soul into it. His was not a forty-hour week. He worked so constantly in his laboratory that it was inevitable that he became a beautiful technician, and throughout his life he had no use for sloppily performed or ill-conceived experiments."

Quoting an aphorism of the eminent 18th Century surgeon, Hunter, and then going on to interpret it, he offers a closer insight into how mastery of craft is attained. " Don't think, try," Hunter had observed. " What he meant," remarks Fleming, " should be clear enough. He did not mean that scientists should not think : only a fool or a worshipper could accuse him of such a statement. What he meant was that scientists should not pursue their speculations without proving every point in their argument as it arises. This is what Pasteur did—he proved by experiment the validity of every step in the formation of his theories. Consequently nothing that he said is ever likely to be contradicted."

But there are also the interventions of chance. " If something unusual happens, don't just cast it away. Most of these things are not important, but you never know when fortune is handing you a prize." It is a favourite theme of his : luck has a place in life, but luck is elusive and will knock only at the doors of those ready for the visit.

Fleming was born and brought up in the 19th Century, the " Wonderful Century " of science, and his character grew naturally, marked by the robust individualism of the stock from which he was bred. Yet his mind and outlook belong

With
Sir Almroth Wright

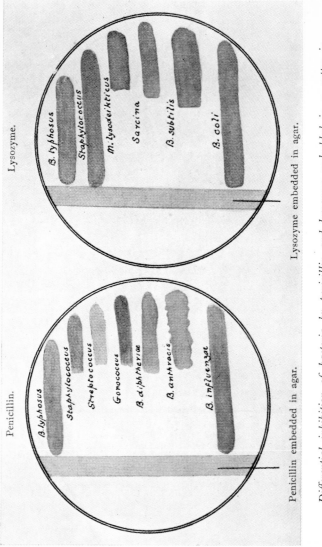

Penicillin.

Lysozyme.

Penicillin embedded in agar.

Lysozyme embedded in agar.

Differential inhibition of bacteria by penicillin and lysozyme embedded in a gutter in an agar plate

to the 20th Century. "I am not a scholar, just a bacteriologist." And again, addressing the boys of Marr College, Troon : " I am not going to tell you how to get on in business or politics because I do not know anything about it, but about medicine . . . " He talks as the specialist in an era of specialization whose life is spent within the undisturbed detachment of a laboratory in the service of his own branch of science, without ranging the widest horizons of knowledge and natural philosophy as was the habit of 19th Century scientists. He has never cultivated a modish intellectualism, his tastes in reading are catholic, from paper-backed thrillers to the gravest expositions of contemporary life. Remonstrance from his friend, Ronald Gray, about this lack of literary eclecticism only drew from him a smile and did nothing to change the habit.

There is little in the sedate presentation of his superb discovery of lysozyme and of the inventiveness he had lavished in searching out its intricate functions and multifarious qualities to convey his feelings at so critical a moment. It is possible to guess at suppressed excitements as he watched the clandestine processes of Nature unfolding before his perceptive vision, Nature as luxuriant inwardly as outwardly, her strange even beautiful order of worlds within worlds ; it is possible to sense the crush of ideas swimming in his brain and their scrupulous selection and rejection. He had helpers, but he stood inescapably alone, deep in introspective solitude, improvising, trying and casting aside, balancing hope and despair, wonder and bafflement, through the long watches of the days and into the nights. Dreams burn bright and then the flames sink low as the winds which have fanned so many hopes die away. But there remains the " glory of a good piece of work ", touched with its own pathos when it turns out that the substance cannot be employed therapeutically.

If only time could mysteriously have been telescoped and the fifteen years to come brought within the survey of the then present ! But all was silence, and there is no respite for mortal creatures. They must perforce keep travelling towards nameless destinations, pin-pointed on no charts. For Fleming new tasks lay ahead.

" I don't think my work on penicillin is the best I've ever done," he has declared, " but it is the one that got into the papers." When he gave the Linacre Lecture many years afterwards, he revealed that in speaking of his best work he had in mind some experiments he had carried out soon after he had come upon lysozyme. An account of these was communicated by Sir Almroth Wright to the Royal Society in November 1923 under the title : "A Comparison of the Activities of Antiseptics on Bacteria and on Leucocytes", and it appeared in the *Proceedings* of the Royal Society during the following year. It was a further extension of his interest in the natural defences of the body and in antiseptics, matters always dominant in his mind. He had shown how chemicals interfered with the phagocytosis of bacteria by the leucocytes ; he now dealt with their effect upon the bactericidal power of the leucocytes themselves, which have such lethal action on microbes. And he utilized new and fascinating techniques for his purposes.

Taking up some blood into a capillary tube, he allowed it to stand in the incubator for an hour, during which time the leucocytes emigrated from the clot and adhered to the walls of the capillary tube. He then expelled the clot, and in its place drew up a weak suspension of staphylococci in serum. He sealed his tube and, laying it in a horizontal position, incubated it for twenty-four hours. When he examined it he found that only one or two colonies of the microbe had developed, whereas in his control tube which did not contain leucocytes, a hundred or more white, wooly staphylococcal colonies had formed. It was Sir Almroth Wright who had devised this fashion of preparing a tube containing leucocytes, and he had called it the " lined tube ". It was a most dramatic demonstration of the bactericidal power of leucocytes.

Employing a different device of Sir Almroth Wright's, the slide cell, he demonstrated with equally dramatic effect the anti-staphylococcal action of the blood. The culture-cells in this method are made from two microscopic slides separated by means of five narrow strips of vaseline paper arranged at intervals transversely to the long axis of the slides. These strips of paper thus divide the space between the two slides into four very thin compartments or cells, open at each end, which will contain rather more than 50 c.mm. of blood. Taking some human blood he added staphylococci to it, in the proportion of a hundred of these cocci to 50 c.mm. of blood. Introducing 50 c.mm. of this mixture into his cells, he incubated them, to find that only two or three colonies developed in each of the cells. On the other hand, if he destroyed the bactericidal action of the leucocytes before incubation, say, by heating to a temperature of 48° C., all the cocci he had implanted grew out. It was a method which also furnished him with a very convenient way of measuring the effect of chemical solutions on the bactericidal power of leucocytes.

From such experiments he has able to show :

That carbolic acid in a concentration of one in four hundred will almost completely destroy the bactericidal power of human leucocytes, while, at the same time, it has practically no inhibitory action on the growth of staphylococci, used as a test microbe.

That even the momentary application of antiseptics of various kinds to the leucocytes is sufficient to destroy their bactericidal power.

That in defribinated blood, out of fifty-six cocci implanted one colony only grew in the control cell, whereas with concentrations of carbolic acid from one in twenty thousand to one in two thousand five hundred the results were not materially different from the control.

He called this range of dilution, where the antiseptic solution had no effect on the bacteria or on the antibacterial power of the blood, the " Indifferent Zone". In the cell containing a concentration of the antiseptic of 1 in 1,280, there was a great increase in the number of colonies, and in the cell which contained 1 in 640 carbolic acid, every staphylococcus implanted grew out. This he termed an "Anti-bactericidal Zone ", where the antiseptic, far from having an inhibitory action on the bacteria, increased the growth because it interfered with or destroyed the bactericidal power of the blood. Finally, in the cell containing 1 in 320 carbolic acid, no colonies developed, and here he assumed that, though the antibacterial power of the blood is destroyed, the antiseptic was in such concentration that it sufficed to inhibit the growth of bacteria. This, he suggested, might be called the "Antiseptic Zone". The outstanding fact was that with nearly all the antiseptics he tested, an "Anti-bactericidal Zone" was manifest, though it varied with each kind of substance.

It was about this time in the medical mode to give intra-venous injections of some of these chemicals in cases of septicaemia, but Fleming was extremely sceptical of such treatment. "Formalin," he said, by way of example, "has in the past been used as an intravenous injection in the treatment of pulmonary tubercle, but here again it can be seen (in experiments he had performed) that with a concentration of 1 in 6,400, the bactericidal power of the blood is seriously interfered with, so that the bacteria grow out freely, while in lesser concentration it is without action."

Shaw, who had always watched the doings of the medical world with both interest and suspicion, reserved some of his most punishing observations for this formalin treatment, which Fleming had condemned as unavailing. He wrote : " In the first frenzy of microbe killing . . . formalin was squirted into the circulation of consumptives until it was discovered that formalin nourishes the tubercle bacillus handsomely and kills men. The popular theory of disease is the common medical theory : namely that every disease has its microbe duly created in the Garden of Eden, and has been steadily propagating itself and producing widening circles of malignant disease ever since. It was plain from the first that if this had been even approximately true, the whole human race would have been wiped out by the plague long ago, and that every epidemic, instead of fading out as mysteriously as it rushed in, would spread over the whole world."

A little later a drug called Sanocrysin was put up as a cure for tuberculosis, causing a flutter of excitement among doctors and among sufferers from the disease, but Fleming who regarded its claims with his usual caution was soon forced to disillusion those who had begun to put their faith in it. He has said :

"This was introduced with a great flare of trumpets as a remedy for tuberculosis. I was present at the meeting which inaugurated the campaign in England. We were told how in infinitesimal concentrations it killed the tubercle bacillus ; how, when it was injected intravenously so many tubercle bacilli were killed that the patient was poisoned with his own dead bacilli and how, to combat this, a special anti-tuberculous serum had to be injected. It seemed wonderful.

"We proceeded at once to test the efficacy of Sanocrysin as a germicide to the tubercle bacillus in human blood. Sanocrysin in various dilutions was mixed with human blood infected with tubercle bacilli and the mixtures were incubated for some days, after which the blood-clots were decolorized and stained. Fry has published the results obtained which showed that in the concentrations of Sanocrysin which could be obtained in the body and even in much higher concentrations, the drug has no influence whatever on the growth of tubercle bacilli.

"Now when Sanocrysin is discussed in the treatment of tuberculosis, there is no mention of the wholesale slaughter of the bacilli by the direct action of the chemical. No anti-tuberculous serum need be given to neutralize the poison of the dead bacilli. Its reputed beneficial effect is attributed to some mysterious change which occurs in the body after its injection."

There was undoubtedly much vague and flabby thinking in medical circles of the day about so-called germicides, and in an address to the Royal Society of Medicine, hinting at his despair of the topic ever being understood as plainly as he understood it, he attempted to dissipate the fogs which lay about it :

"What do we mean by the term 'germicide'? It is obvious that a germicide must be something which will kill microbes, and I have to thank my master, Sir Almroth Wright, for this definition : 'a germicide is a substance which will enter into destructive combination with a microbe'. I think we shall all agree that it would be wrong to class as germicides substances which in the concentration employed do not kill microbes *per se*, but when injected into the circulation are reputed to undergo or induce some possibly mysterious change by which the antibacterial power of the blood is enhanced. Otherwise all manner of substances would have to be classed as germicides, for instance, nuclein, vaccines, and hypertonic salt solution. We may think that vaccines are potent agents with which to cope with infections, but this discussion is not one on vaccine therapy. It may seem to you ridiculous to mention those things, but at the last discussion on antiseptics which I attended the surgeon who opened it dealt entirely with substances having about the same germicidal power of typhoid vaccine.

" The definition of a germicide as a substance which will directly destroy microbes leaves us with a comparatively simple problem. We can estimate the germicidal power of any substance in blood outside the body by the simple method of adding to it infected blood, and after a lapse of time noting whether or not the bactericidal power of the blood is increased. In the body there are certain factors which may interfere with the action of any germicide which may be introduced, but it is absolutely inconceivable that any chemical will act as a direct germicide in the circulating blood when it fails in a like concentration to increase the bactericidal power of blood in a test-tube.

" For a germicide to be successful in killing bacteria in the circulating blood two essential conditions must be fulfilled. It may be that even if they are fulfilled, the practical result will be negligible, but if they are not, failure is inevitable. These conditions are :—It must be possible *with safety* (1) to obtain a concentration of germicide in blood which is lethal to the microbes ; (2) to maintain such a concentration sufficiently long for the microbes to be killed.

" Another important point to be considered is whether the germicides act only on one or two species of microbes or on many. The importance of this last condition is often lost sight of in practice, and we find an antiseptic which has been shown to have a powerful lethal effect on one microbe used to combat an infection with another organism to which it is relatively inert."

If chemical germicides lacked efficacy, was there a means of fortifying the blood so that it could better resist invasion by microbes ? Fleming turned to investigate the results of variations in its salt-content. He first tried out intravenous injections of hypertonic salt solution on rabbits, and afterwards, choosing a boy suffering from phthisis, gave him similar injections with benefits that were confirmed in other cases. From these experiments he concluded :

That leucocytes only function efficiently within certain limits of salt concentration, and that when the salt content falls below or rises above these limits, the leucocytes do not emigrate and do not phagocyte or destroy bacteria.

That when a large amount of salt is injected into an animal so that the salt content of the blood is materially raised, the normal bactericidal power is temporarily lost, but that after a few hours it is greatly enhanced. When smaller doses are injected, the preliminary fall in the bactericidal power is avoided, but the subsequent rise is marked and in man the injection of an amount of salt so little that when diluted with the blood it would only increase the salt content by 0.01 per cent., causes after three hours a great rise in the bactericidal power of the blood. So far, the experiments threw little light on the reason for this astonishing rise in the bactericidal power.

That the intravenous injection of hypertonic salt solution has been used in cholera and other diseases with a view to increasing the blood volume, but the result shown by these tests show that such injections may produce benefit, not only by virtue of their increased fluid content, but also by conferring on the patient's blood much greater power of destroying the infecting bacteria.

He had thus demonstrated that the bactericidal power of the human blood could be increased by the administration of intravenous injections of hypertonic salt solution, but he took this vital question further when in a paper he read before the Royal Society of Medicine on " The Bactericidal Power of Human Blood and Some Methods of Altering It ", he described other means of achieving the same effect. Summed up, this alteration could be brought about by :

1. Increasing the opsonic power of the blood-fluids by vaccine therapy.

2. Increasing the efficiency of the leucocytes by giving blood transfusions.

3. Increasing the number of leucocytes by injection of a derivative of yeast called nuclein.

4. The employment of physical methods, such as light. (Animals irradiated with the carbon arc or mercury vapour lamp, after a while acquire an increased bactericidal power in the blood. Exposure to sunlight would produce the same effect. Two hours after a sun-bath a normal man developed an exceptionally high bactericidal capacity which was maintained for several hours. But if the exposure was over-prolonged, it would fall very much instead of rising. Dosage was therefore extremely important.)

5. Chemical methods. Drugs injected would combine with and destroy an infecting microbe. It was on this basis that the whole Chemotherapy of Ehrlich and his followers was based. It is successful in syphilis, in trypanosomiasis (sleeping sickness), malaria and amoebic dysentery, but not so successful in the common bacterial infections. There is also the type of drug which acts indirectly as an antiseptic by affecting the bacteria and making them susceptible to destruction by the leucocytes.

But there was no question of the superiority of the natural antiseptic over any of the common chemical substances.

During these busy years between 1922 and 1938, Fleming had published the results of enquiries into certain technical problems, and into certain issues relative to lysozyme, but what emerges above all else is his profound belief in the natural protective mechanisms of the body, a belief enhanced by his discovery of that substance. It was a profession of faith when he declared :

"I am certain that the potency of the natural mechanism whereby we are protected against the invasion of microbes is not generally appreciated. Possibly because we, in the practice of our profession, are constantly dealing with people who are infected, we lose sight of the vast bulk of the population who, in spite of the artificial conditions in which they live, escape serious infection. The resistance against infection must be very perfect when we consider that our mouths, throats and alimentary tracts harbour potentially pathogenic microbes, and that there is only one layer of epithelial cells between the contents of the intestine, including Bacillus coli, streptococci and gas-gangrene bacilli, and the deeper tissues in which, given favourable conditions, these bacteria can flourish and give rise to deadly infections.

"The protective mechanisms are of different kinds. First of all, there is the mechanical resistance of the integument. Then, there is some mechanism whereby extraneous microbes are rapidly destroyed on the skin. The exact nature of this is not clear, but possibly it is related to a protective mechanism which I described in 1922. This is an antibacterial ferment, lysozyme, which is generally distributed throughout the body and which is present in great concentration in some of the human secretions, e.g., tears, nasal mucus, etc. The mechanical obstruction of the integument and the antibacterial content of the secretions and covering tissues furnish a first line of defence, but if they are defeated then we have the phagocytic activity of the wandering cells of the body and the antibacterial and anti-toxic action of the blood and of the blood-fluids."

But this was, in truth, the restatement of a view he had steadfastly held, based upon an idea cherished by Pasteur and his disciples, who believed also that in medical research infinite prospects lie among natural antibacterial agents, especially those produced by other micro-organisms. And his own master, Sir Almroth Wright, had not only subscribed to this opinion but had been responsible for its advancement when he, with the help of Fleming and others, had begun the practice of vaccine therapy, because vaccine therapy means evoking the highest possible response from the instruments provided by Nature in the human body for fending off bacterial attack.

Fleming's mind with its visionary cast could, as he had shown, penetrate the solid crusts of the ' cake of custom '. While remaining true to itself and drawing nourishment from its own proper roots, it could project itself to grasp the formatives of new styles of thought in which healthy scepticism was eroding the vastly assured claims of manufactured panaceas. He was impressed not by how much was known in medicine but by how little. In any event, though antiseptics might be found to kill off the greater number of infecting bacteria or to frustrate their growth, it was ultimately the body which had to destroy the residue by mobilizing its own essential defences. To him this was a cardinal principle.

CHAPTER XI

THE GREAT SCIENTIST

FLEMING WAS now Assistant Director of the Inoculation Department at St. Mary's Hospital, and in 1928 he was appointed Professor of Bacteriology in the University of London. Thus at the age of forty-seven he had attained a pre-eminent position in his own sphere as a bacteriologist. But the pleasure of success was tempered with sorrow, for his mother had died in that year. She had been in London until 1922, except for a short time during the First World War, and had only left to go and live in Scotland after his marriage.

For him work and responsibilities had increased, but he still found time for satisfying recreations. At his home in Chelsea he had the background of a family man ; he had his wife and small son to whom he devoted his attentions at the end of each day ; there were exchanges of visits from friends, an occasional game of bridge, an evening at the Chelsea Arts Club. Sometimes he painted in oils, sometimes played a game of golf from a handicap of twelve, and enjoyed his hobby of photography.

Shortly after the First World War had ended, he had bought a country house at Barton Mills in Suffolk, named "The Dhoon", with a stone-flagged path leading up to its pleasantly carved front door, flanked by two stone seats. Whenever he could, he spent week-ends and other holidays there, indulging that love of the countryside and of the open-air which had been bred in him during childhood days among the Ayrshire moors. He went boating on the river nearby and fished for gudgeon and pike ; he grew flowers and vegetables, sawed up logs, thought of gadgets he could make for himself and played the good handyman.

When friends came to stay, he took a vast delight in challenging the local train in his motor car, but since the ancient locomotive had seen its best days and could now only puff along the single track at a pace appropriate to its age, there was hardly any danger of his being beaten from an equal start. However, his friends suspected him of hanging back deliberately until it had left the station a certain time, so that he could better balance the contest by a self-imposed handicap. Certainly he was exhilarated by the race, happy as he sped through the keen air along the country road.

In Wright's department at the hospital that indefinable *éclat* which surrounds new enterprises had inevitably diminished, and there was now a steady march against the resistance of stubborn problems. Something had changed during the enforced interruption of the war years which in the aftermath defied restoration. No longer did so many doctors from all corners of the world flock to St. Mary's and bring to it a once cosmopolitan flavour ; young men at home seemed less ready to abandon the after-war pursuits in which they were caught up for the seclusions of a life of science ; even the fresh facts and theories which Wright advanced with enthusiasm were accorded smaller notice. Yet, inside the laboratory the usual healthy freedom of thought persisted ; some degree of corporate endeavour was essential to the general plans for research, but within that wide framework, Fleming could pursue his own designs.

The voyage until he discovered lysozyme had been long, and before and since then he had touched many fresh shores. But it was by no means accomplished. He was still afloat, master of his craft as the winds blew him towards wider waters. Heart and mind in harmony, he stood four-square in the immoveable structure of his character. Reason, imagination and intuition, each strong in itself, were yet finely blended. Destiny had chosen him for the most exclusive of its preferments because by assiduous cultivation of what lay within him he had made himself so fitting a recipient.

Dr. Charles Nicolle in his *Destin des Maladies Infectieuse* defines the importance of these three qualities in the scientist when he says :

" Whatever problems we attack with our minds, our surest arm in resolving them is the power of reasoning, logic. And certainly we should not turn up our noses at reasoning in the study of diseases. It plays a considerable and necessary part among our attainments. Yet we must guard against delivering ourselves up to it entirely in order to light our way through unknown territories and bring enlightenment to our conceptions of to-morrow.

" Logic based on observation allows us to sum up a problem, to investigate it, to extend its limits, to seek out its connections and analogies with questions already settled. A new fact acquired, logic makes it clear and complete and sets it in place. Thanks to reasoning, we can group together isolated facts, judge the gaps, give ourselves an insight into the whole, thereby making ready for other conquests.

" But to make such conquests, no longer count on reasoning, for reason hugs the shore.

" If there is to be that bound forward towards true discovery within the scope of whatever is being explored, it is imagination and intuition which will enable us to make it.

" For it to be otherwise, life would have to be logical, and we know that it is not. Life is blind, so where is reason and intelligence to be applied in what is but the result of circumstances ? Life knows no reason, it seeks only the possibilities of expressing itself. . ."

Another writer on scientific matters, Mr. Chapman Pincher, has formulated a scale for the assessment of greatness in science. " The few who have been truly great in science " he declares, " owed their greatness to four outstanding qualities :

CURIOSITY : A deep-seated drive which could not be stifled and could be satisfied only by the thrill of discovery.

INSIGHT : An unusual ability to get straight to the hub of the problems which fretted their minds.

INGENUITY : A flair for devising simple yet convincing experiments to test their hunches.

PERSISTENCE : A stubborn determination to keep at grips with problems in spite of seemingly insuperable difficulties.

" One of these four qualities has usually dominated the others in each great scientist," he continues. " Lord Rutherford, the founder of atomic science owed his success mainly to astonishing ingenuity ; with Sir Isaac Newton insight was the predominating quality; in Marie Curie's case it was extraordinary persistence that saw her through. But without a fair measure of all four qualities none of these people would have achieved greatness."

Medical research, however, occupies a special place, for it is not curiosity alone that drives men and women to adopt it as their life's work; its votaries are drawn towards it by feelings of humanity and compassion which they hope one day to assuage a little by some discovery which might reduce in strength the acids of human suffering. Wright had called it " a pain in the mind ", and Fleming himself frequently showed how sensible he was to this altruism. Researchers in medicine are almost always keenly aware of our humiliating susceptibility to illnesses, they hold a particular resentment against our proneness to physical decay. They might, perhaps, see life as one of Aldous Huxley's characters in *Those Barren Leaves* saw it :

> " The greatest tragedy of the spirit is the thought that sooner or later it succumbs to the flesh. Sooner or later every soul is stifled by the sick body ; sooner or later there are no more thoughts, but only pain and vomitting and stupor . . . Death, you can't get over the fact that, at the end of everything, the flesh gets hold of the spirit and squeezes the life out of it so that man turns into something that's no better than a whining sick animal."

It is in this condition of mind that curiosity for them gains urgency, endowing them with an ineluctable impulse to wrest from Nature the means of preserving the body, of healing its afflictions.

In Fleming curiosity was innate ; in his youth it had been directed towards what he described as " wild nature ", and in thinking up various contrivances " to see how they would work ". Later that curiosity became centred upon the problems of bacteriology. He heard from Wright, his *allumeur d'âme*, about anti-typhoid vaccine which had saved numberless lives, he heard about phagocytosis and the opsonic power of the blood serum. It was so alluring a field for the exercise of his curiosity that he joined Wright's staff without any delay, the day after he qualified.

Mr. Pincher describes this curiosity as " a deep-seated drive which could not be stifled and could be satisfied only by the thrill of discovery." What was Fleming's life but an unending series of experiments rewarded by a good crop of discoveries, each with its own value for medical science, though none might have made headline news ? Only his inquisitiveness made him culture his own nasal secretion when he had a cold, and that led him to lysozyme ; only a deep-seated drive remorselessly carried him on to unravel the potent secrets of the body's natural defences and show up the impotence of chemical antiseptics.

" Insight " is Mr. Pincher's second demand, " an unusual ability to get straight to the hub of the problems which fretted their minds." What insight had prompted Fleming to make a culture of his own nasal secretion and so progress to the discovery of lysozyme ? What insight prejudiced him against the well-accepted belief in chemical antiseptics, held as an article of faith handed down by the great Lister himself? The problem that fretted his mind had consistently been the same : Nature's processes were not clearly enough understood, the astonishing natural protection offered the human organism not well enough appreciated. How could man be given immunity against the various diseases which threatened him ? How could Nature be assisted in fighting off a disease once it had been contracted ? He had seen deep into the workings of natural protective mechanisms, had elaborated them and helped to enlarge the prevailing conceptions of immunology.

" Ingenuity : A flair for devising simple yet convincing experiments to test their hunches." This is Mr. Pincher's third stipulation. Fleming's colleagues have without exception attested his partiality for simple apparatus and simple methods in the laboratory, and what experiments more simple, more beautiful or more convincing than those he had performed in France ? There was his classic demonstration that microbes grew more profusely in serum to which carbolic acid had been added than in plain serum ; there was his ingenious simulation of a wound by drawing out spikes from the lower end of a test tube to show that its germ population multiplied even after flushing out with antiseptics, just as they would in a wound with its complex and inaccessible indentations. And every stage of his enquiries into the nature of lysozyme was supported by thorough-going tests of model simplicity.

"A flair for devising simple yet convincing experiments to test their hunches." Here perhaps was the quality which in Fleming dominates those others, and which Mr. Pincher expects of his great men of science.

Finally, Mr. Pincher demands : " Persistence : A stubborn determination to keep at grips with problems in spite of seemingly insuperable difficulties ". Tenacity advertises itself eloquently in the cast of Fleming's features ; it was a characteristic inherited from his Scottish forbears, and its presence was abundantly exemplified in his sure progress through life, with success added to success, and in his steadfast accumulation of knowledge about the scientific problems he examined. He pursued his investigations into the effects of chemical antiseptics and into the body's natural defences over years, he pursued his enquiries into lysozyme over years.

However, in the end Mr. Pincher modifies the four-point scale he had adopted to measure greatness in science. He says : " Maybe the tempo and scope of modern science have been stepped up so much in the last fifteen years that a four-point scale for greatness is outdated. Scientific progress now depends on teamwork rather than isolated geniuses working in backrooms. So the great men of modern science may be those with the power to think out projects and inspire others to carry them out. Exceptional capacity for leadership may be their rare virtue."

Fleming himself has never doubted how research ought to be conducted and how scientific progress can continue. At a dinner given in his honour at the Mayo Foundation House in Rochester, Minnesota, on July 16th, 1945, he remarked :

"There are different ways of conducting research. One method which has been adopted is to collect a lot of money or some firm puts up a lot of money and says, ' Now, we will do research '. They collect somebody as the master and a lot of people as the lesser ones. They tell the master, ' We want research on some particular thing ', and he has to do it. He tells the other ones what they have to do. It is labelled research. I don't know how much that is new comes out of it. Suppose you have a team of ten people and they are going to do research on some particular thing. They pool their ideas. They all talk around the table. What are you going to get? Are you going to get the sum total of those or the average? I venture to suggest you are going to get the average. With ten ordinary mortals you don't get anything new. You get some work but you don't initiate anything. . .

" Suppose, however, I had been part of a team at the beginning and I was being directed on a certain piece of research which I was engaged on, and the accident happened which led to penicillin. In these circumstances I would have chucked the thing away and gone on with my research. Fortunately I was an individual. That's where a team might have been disastrous. A team is fine when you have something to go on, but when you have nothing to go on—well, I should think a team is the worst possible way of starting, and it is impossible to start out to find something brand new with a team.

" I know that certain industrial places—well, say in England —put up a certain amount of money for research and hire a team. They often direct them on the particular problems they are going to work out. This is a very good way of employing a certain number of people, paying salaries and not getting very much in return. If they simply want to take something already discovered and work out details for a cheaper way of making it, that is the way to do it.

" If you want to start something new, I am sure you have to subsidize an individual, and it seems to me a very good thing that in all places, such as here, academic institutions or industrial institutions, everybody has a certain amount of routine work to do. He doesn't sit down and play at research from morning to night. He has a job to do. If he is a senior, perhaps it only takes a little of his time. If he is a junior, it takes a bit more. And then he may find time for research and discover something new. Some will and some won't. I think that is the only way to do research and it doesn't matter whether it is here or in England. The way to do it is to give a man a free hand for a portion of his time and let him do as he will."

Even before he discovered penicillin, Fleming by any scale bore the marks of greatness in science. He was an isolated genius in a back-room, of whom it has been written : " The man himself with his leisurely, easy-going manner, his seeming

Arriving at le Bourget to be honoured by the Paris Académie de Médicine. Fleming with the distinguished French scientists (left to right) Vallery-Radot, Trefouels and Lepine.

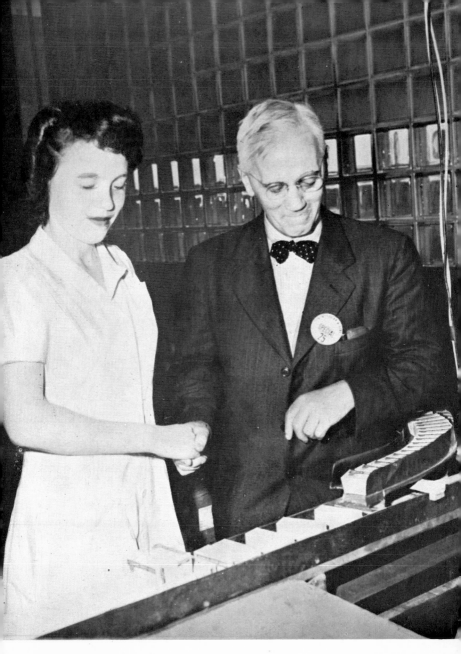

Receiving the congratulations of an employee of one of the first American firms to prod
penicillin commercially

lack of efficiency, does not reflect the methods of the machine-age ; his working quarters are little reminiscent of the sterilized sanctums of American researchers. He brings to mind the horse-and-buggy doctor who kept his instruments in a dark closet but who regarded his patients as human beings first of all. It is from the human standpoint that he looks upon research. it is the man bending over the microscope and holding the test-tubes to the light who counts. While modern instruments are essential in the development of science, they are useless without the brain to control them."

The laboratory in which he discovered penicillin has been described as " dingy and dun-coloured." It was not spacious, it was small and cramped. Afterwards used as a rest-room for doctors on night-duty at St. Mary's, its lack of size leapt to the eye. It could take two single beds and precious little else. Yet its very compactness was not without advantage. Fleming's apparatus, his table, his typewriter, his books and papers were all easily and quickly to hand. His own reply to slightly astonished Americans who had heard about this primitive accommodation came when he went to their country and was shown their ' sterilized sanctums ', shining and spotless. " Wonderful, but penicillin could never have been discovered in a lab. like this one ! " Of course, no spores could live in that uncontaminated air ! It was good-natured chaff, but it carried the whispered undertones of the sardonic that touches his sense of humour.

Another American newspaperman, he relates, " described my own laboratory as like the backroom of an old-fashioned drug store. What would they have said about Pasteur's attic? It only shows that it is not the grandeur of the laboratory but the grandeur of the man that matters, and that the marble halls so common in certain parts of the world are quite secondary to the brain of the worker."

His attitude resembled Pasteur's own, for that great man was once very shocked to see a collaborator had acquired two fine armchairs for his laboratory, one of them a rocking-chair. He could not understand the need for such physical comforts.

In the late summer of 1928, Fleming, now forty-seven years

old, sat working in his own unspectacular laboratory over-looking an unprepossessing London neighbourhood. Six years before, when he had discovered lysozyme, the air had quivered for a moment. But even in the present stillness he was ready to " stretch forth his hand and try to grasp the hem when he heard the garment of God rustling through events."

CHAPTER XII

THE WINDS OF HEAVEN

"IN 1928," says Fleming, "I hit on penicillin. The very first stage in the discovery of penicillin was due to a stroke of good fortune . . . "

Again he will have it that the favours of fortune have blazed down upon him ; the dusts of prosaic daily labour settle and one fine day there are signs of flowering. But such signs are visible only to those who have the eyes with which to see them. And into his self-effacing statement he has to admit an essential qualification ; there are, after all, other elements as well as luck :

"If my mind had not been in a reasonably perceptive state, I would not have paid any attention to it. I might have been in a bad temper, say after a quarrel with my wife ; I might have just have become engaged and my mind might have been full of the young woman, or I might have been suffering from the after effects of too heavy a meal and been mentally too sluggish to notice it or do anything about it." But even a reasonably perceptive state of mind is not enough, as he goes on to point out :

" Before you can notice any strange happening you have got to be a good workman, you have got to be a master of your craft."

Workmanship, mastery of craft, luck, a perceptive mind . . . Once before, in discovering lysozyme, he had looked at a culture plate and to his amazement found clear spaces where his tears had inhibited microbial growth : " Thus, it was with a mind accustomed to seeing hiatuses in bacterial cultures that he gazed on a fateful Petri dish contaminated with an unknown mould." He had, in addition, another curious asset to serve him well on such occasions, illustrated by the story of a game of snooker he played at the Chelsea Arts Club one day. Looking at his watch, he realised suddenly that it was later than he thought. " I'll get into a row with the missus if I don't hurry along," he joked, " we'd better finish this off." He was never considered an outstandingly good player, but when his turn came, he took up his cue, potted every ball remaining on the table, apparently without effort, put his cue away, bade his amazed companions good night and went home. It is an example of a capacity he possesses for digging deep into hidden reserves within himself and calling upon them when occasion demands.

Now, there is a class of mould which botanists call Penicillium, because of its brush-like appearance. The common blue mould such as is seen on bread or cheese is a Penicillium It starts off as minute spores about the size of a blood corpuscle or a little less. Then they send out sprouts, and these grow and branch and branch again until they become a mould colony. The blue colour is due to its sending up special reproductive processes into the air : they branch and then branch again, and at the end of the branches the spores are budded off, millions of them. Those spores blow around and settle down where the wind takes them, and if they find a nice comfortable spot, they grow. It is a good job they do not all grow because one little mould colony has millions of spores. If they all grew, everybody would be mouldy indeed.

The summer of 1928 happened to be cool and damp and encouraged the presence of these mould spores in greater profusion than hotter, drier airs. At the time, Fleming had to write an article on staphylococci for the projected Medical Research Council " System of Bacteriology ", and he was confirming certain results published by a fellow-scientist on the variation of staphylococcus colonies. This involved the examination of culture plates with a dissecting microscope, and on each occasion they were examined the cover had to be removed. So, while its cover was off for a moment, a mould spore directed by the winds of Heaven, landed in one of the culture plates, a shallow, glass Petri dish, only four inches in diameter, which stood among others on the bench of his small laboratory. "As soon as you open a culture plate," says Fleming, " you are asking for trouble. Things drop from the air. One of those bits of trouble happened to be penicillin

. . . A mould spore, coming from I don't know where, dropped on the plate. That didn't excite me, I had often seen such contamination before. But what I had never seen before was staphylococci undergoing lysis around the contaminating colony. Obviously something extraordinary was happening.

" With the background that I had, this was far more interesting to me than staphylococcal research, so I switched promptly. I am now glad that for years my interest had been directed to antiseptics and that some years before I had found in a somewhat similar manner another naturally occurring antiseptic, lysozyme. But for that previous experience it is likely that I would have thrown the plate away as many bacteriologists must have done before . . . Instead of casting out the contaminated culture with appropriate language, I made some investigations."

Thus a master of his craft with his perceptive genius had spotted that something extraordinary was happening in one of his Petri dishes. How many chances are involved in that simple statement ? As Fleming has said : " There are thousands of different moulds and there are thousands of different bacteria, and that chance put that mould in the right spot at the right time was like winning the Irish sweep." What an extraordinary concatenation of events that he happened to be working with staphylococci when the mould-spore fell among them for they were microbes highly sensitive to the action of the mysterious substance produced by the mould.

Nevertheless, it is necessary to view the chance-element of his discovery in its proper perspective, and a comment of his does just this : " So far as I know, there is nothing in the literature which would lead any worker to suspect that a substance with the chemical constitution of penicillin would have any value as an antibacterial agent. It had to happen by chance, and it was fortunate that the chance presented itself to me. A mould colony which appeared as a contamination on a culture plate made such a change in the colonies of staphylococci which were on the plate that something had to be done about it. It had nothing to do with the problem which I was at the moment investigating—that was a very minor one . . . "

Moreover, as a scientist friend said to him in a letter : " Though Lady Luck may fly in at the window, she has a way of eluding the undiscerning—believe me !—and settling where she's not unlooked for." Or yet again, as Pasteur held : " In the fields of observation chance only favours the mind prepared." And Fleming's mind had been prepared by long application and training in Wright's laboratories, by an undiverted interest in antiseptics, heightened during the First World War, and by his discovery of that unique substance, lysozyme.

It is reported that when Fleming first noted the dissolving microbes round the mould in his Petri dish, he went to a colleague and said : " Now look at this, this is very interesting. I like this sort of thing, it might be important." His colleague looked, and handing back the plate replied : " Yes, very interesting." Later he was to confess that his had been merely an expression of polite interest. " I thought it was something like lysozyme," he admitted.

But undeterred, Fleming commenced a systematic investigation of the substance, which had so strange an effect on microbes, the moment after he had made his acute observation. " I subcultured the mould," he says, " and got it in pure culture. When you have a pure culture you can play with it." In the laboratory, the bacteriologist's chief implement is a piece of wire on the end of a stick, called the platinum loop. Having heated this in order to sterilize it, he touched the mould which had blown in and dropped a few spores into a test tube containing a medium in which he knew moulds would flourish. The spores grew into a pure culture of the mould.

Next he planted some spores on an agar plate and allowed them to develop at room temperature for four to five days, after which a variety of bacteria were streaked across the plate radially to the mould colony. Some of them grew right up to the mould, but other stopped short of it. This showed that the mould produced an antibacterial substance readily diffusible in agar, which acted only on certain microbes. Here were results not dissimilar from those produced with lysozyme, except that different microbes were affected. The microbes affected by lysozyme would have been non-pathogenic, but now the ones inhibited were pathogenic—some of the common pathogenic microbes. "That made it interesting," was Fleming's comment, " here was a mould that did something which might be useful."

The mould was then planted on a fluid medium, broth, to see whether the antibacterial substance would appear in the fluid. It grew as a felted mass on the surface, leaving the liquid perfectly clear, and after a few days it imparted an intense yellow colour to the broth. Although colourless, names like " yellow magic " and " mould gold " were invented to describe penicillin, the yellow pigment had nothing to do with it and was an impurity. After a week's growth, the fluid was tested for its antibacterial properties, and the simplest test was one previously used for lysozyme.

" I took some of this clear fluid," says Fleming, " from the week-old culture, embedded it in a gutter in an agar plate and then streaked microbes across the plate, at right-angles to the gutter. The result was similar to that seen when microbes were streaked up to the mould culture ; some of them grew right up to the fluid and some of them didn't grow near it. That showed the mould made something which appeared in the culture fluid and which affected some microbes and not others. Then I made dilutions of the fluid to see how strong the inhibiting substance was and found that dilutions of something close to 1 in 1,000 still inhibited the staphylococcus."

Meanwhile the substance in the fluid had to be named. Fleming's nomenclature was quite orthodox. " I am accused of making a comic name," he remarks, " why call anything penicillin ? It was in accordance with orthodox medical practice. Something was made by a plant-mould of the genus Penicillium, so I called it penicillin. There is another plant, the foxglove, scientific name, digitalis, which makes a powerful drug which we call digitalin. That is a commonly adopted practice and penicillin is a perfectly orthodox name. Well, now, what is Penicillium ? It is quite true that when this work began I knew almost nothing about a Penicillium. We had been taught a little Botany in our early days at the hospital and we heard there was such a thing as a Penicillium, but I did not know much about it." He says again : " We had a little trouble with identification. Our mycologist who put it through its paces called it *Penicillium rubrum*. But it made a bright yellow colour and even with my small knowledge of Latin I thought rubrum (red) did not mean yellow." That name proved to be wrong, and in November 1945 the mycologist wrote a letter to Fleming in which he said : "As I know that you accepted this nomenclature against your better judgment, perhaps you will allow me to write to Dr. Herrell (of the Mayo Clinic in America) stating what I know to be the truth. I . . . am very sorry indeed to have thus misled you into publishing an incorrect statement in your original paper. . . ."

Fleming's first paper on the subject of penicillin was soberly headed : " The Antibacterial Action of Cultures of a Penicillium with Special Reference to their use in the Isolation of B. Influenzae ". (*British Journal of Experimental Pathology*, Volume X, page 226, received for publication on May 10th, 1929.) There he had written : " In its morphology this organism is a Penicillium and in all its characters it most closely resembles P. rubrum. Biourge 1923, (a Belgian who had made the Penicillium group a life-study), states that he has never found P. rubrum in nature and that it is an *animal de laboratoire*. This penicillium is not uncommon in the air of the laboratory." He goes on : "A number of other moulds were grown in broth at room temperature and the culture fluids were tested for antibacterial substances at various intervals up to one month. Of these it was found that only one strain of penicillium produced any inhibitory substance, and that one had exactly the same cultural characters as the original one from the contaminated plate. . . .

" In the rest of this article allusion will constantly be made to experiments with filtrates of broth cultures of this mould, so for convenience and to avoid the repetition of the rather cumbersome phrase, ' Mould broth filtrate ', the name ' penicillin ' will be used. This will denote the filtrate of a broth culture of the particular penicillium with which we are concerned."

He is also at pains to thank the mycologist " for his suggestions as to the identity of the penicillium ". Certainly Fleming was not an expert in moulds, and he could hardly be held responsible for the misnomer. In any case, this particular mould eluded exact identification for some time. It went to a famous Continental mycologist and she called it something else. Later Professor Harold Raistrick of the London School of Hygiene and Tropical Medicine correctly named it *Penicillium notatum* and his opinion was confirmed by Dr. Thom, a leading American mycologist. Dr. Thom found it was not quite identical with his stock culture, but he was right, and many strains of *Penicillium notatum* were subsequently found which make penicillin.

So far experiment had shown that the antibacterial fluid made by the mould was very diffusible in agar. " Now," says Fleming, " there's another thing which interests me in regard to antiseptics ; that is their diffusibility. I had compared the diffusibility of penicillin in an agar plate with that of the older antiseptics such as carbolic acid, iodine and acriflavine. These show little power of diffusion whereas penicillin is extremely diffusible."

He continues : "All the effects of penicillin I have told you about so far relate only to the inhibition of growth of the microbes, but this substance does more than that ; it kills the microbes as well and induces a lytic action." To demonstrate this he took an agar culture plate, planted it with staphylococcus and then punched out discs of agar with a cork borer, which were removed. The holes thus made in the medium were then sealed each with a drop of melted agar, forming cups into which small quantities of fluid from various mould cultures were placed. This was done to compare the penicillin content of the various cultures, which all proved strongly inhibitory, but there were patches where the staphylococci grew copiously. These plates were then left on the bench for a week, when the mould spores which had been in the fluid in the agar cups grew out and produced a fresh supply of penicillin. This resulted in an almost complete lysis of the thick staphylococcal growth on the plate.

Penicillin was thus bacteriostatic (it had the power of arresting the growth of the microbes), it was bactericidal (it had the power of destroying microbes), and it had bacteriolytic properties (it was capable of dissolving microbes), and later, another scientist showed that it had a remarkable effect in modifying the cell division of the bacteria sensitive to it. In a weak solution of penicillin, for example, the bacillus of Welch, instead of showing its normal, shortish appearance, grew out as long threads, and the gonococci in the bloodstream of a patient suffering from gonorrhea after one injection of penicillin showed up large and swollen, having lost their typical shape.

Now came a crucial test. Was it harmful to leucocytes? Was it toxic to animals? It was tested on the cells and found to have no injurious effect on them, unlike chemical antiseptics which were all more destructive to the leucocytes than they were to the microbe. So here was penicillin, about three times as potent as carbolic acid in its inhibitory effect on a microbe like the staphylococcus, and yet it was inocuous so far as the cells were concerned. It was injected into animals such as rabbits and white mice and found to be no more toxic to them than the broth in which the mould had grown. This was something new, and as Fleming has said : " It was this non-toxicity to leucocytes that convinced me that some day it would come into its own as a therapeutic agent, and led me in 1929 to suggest that it might be an efficient antiseptic for application to, or injection into areas infected with penicillin-sensitive microbes."

Thus Fleming, the militant opponent of chemical antiseptics, the ardent believer in the wonderful powers of Nature, for the second time had had revealed to him the extent of those powers. " I have been accused of inventing penicillin," he says, " no man could ever have done that. Nature in the form of a lowly vegetable has been making it for thousands of years. I only discovered it." Hours, days, weeks, and months of patient and rigorous work and meditation followed, among the tensions and pressures, among rising hopes and the flowing tides of exaltation, as experiment after experiment promised that this time the results of his enquiries would find immediate practical application, and illuminate a lifetime dedicated to science and spent for the most part in solitary communion with depths within himself barricaded from the profaner world. Yet a moment of expected climax trembled, revelation was clouded by a cruel paradox. "So far," as he has recorded, "we had a Penicillium which produced in its growth a powerful, selective antibacterial substance readily diffusible in agar, and which was inocuous to laboratory animals and to leucocytes. I christened this substance penicillin.

"But penicillin is a very unstable substance." Here was the disappointment. He continues :

"I was a lone individual—more or less alone. I collected a couple of juniors in a lab. afterwards and we did a little bit of work and got as far as we could. We found out a lot of things about the properties of penicillin and then got completely stuck—short of chemical knowledge. We tried various media which are used in a bacteriological laboratory, but found that the yield was as good in our ordinary broth as in any other. . . ."

So he prepared his broths and brews and sowed them with the mould spores, then he put them into incubators at different temperatures, and was satisfied that they did best when the thermometer stood at 20° C. When he grew it for a week in ordinary broth the liquid showed not the slightest trace of acid ; indeed, the longer it grew the greater the alkilinity. Indeed he reported : "Unless the reaction is adjusted the selective antibacterial action disappears in a few days." Thus the mould that was producing penicillin was also producing the heightening alkilinity which weakened it, so he dealt with the difficulty by adding enough acid to neutralize its alkilinity and even keep it a little on the acid side.

He heated it for an hour at 56° C. and it retained its potency ; he heated it for an hour at 80° C. and it still retained its potency ; he boiled it for a few minutes and it was unaffected ; he boiled it for a whole hour and it lost three-quarters of its vitality. When he steamed it under pressure in an autoclave for twenty minutes at 115° C. it became devitalized, yet it could be passed through a filter of asbestos pads and keep all its qualities. And after each of these trials he assured himself of the results by applying the liquid filtered out from his broths to his test microbes which were staphylococci. If it dissolved the microbes it was because it contained penicillin which was hostile to them ; if they survived it was because the penicillin had vanished. He had chosen the staphylococcus because " it is a very suitable microbe on which to test the broth as it is hardy, lives well in culture, grows rapidly and is very sensitive to penicillin."

He called upon the help of a colleague to try and separate the penicillin from the broth in which it lay. Having evaporated the broth, it could be extracted from the viscous brown residue by using alcohol. It was insoluble in ether and in chloroform but freely soluble in water or weak saline. This was a discouraging line of enquiry.

He learned that the mould only began to give off penicillin on the fifth day. On that day, one drop of the penicillin broth in twenty drops of distilled water destroyed his test microbes. On the sixth day the penicillin was twice as strong ; on the seventh day its strength had multiplied tenfold in comparison with the fifth day ; it now required only one drop of penicillin in two hundred drops of distilled water to wipe out the test microbes. Between the seventh day and the eighth day, its strength was again doubled, for after twenty-four hours one drop in five hundred of distilled water was all it took to kill the test germs, and this was the peak of its potency. After that it daily grew weaker and ceased to be exuded from the ageing mould. Moreover, its antibacterial power fell when kept at room temperature.

When he picked off one of the vivid yellow droplets that appeared on the felted surface of the broth, round about the fifth day, he was astonished to find that one drop in twenty thousand of distilled water could destroy the test microbes. Here perhaps might be the minute repositories of this tantalizing substance.

And meanwhile he knew it could kill off the germs which caused pneumonia, diphtheria and gonorrhea, as well as streptococci and staphylococci, which were responsible for other infective complaints like sore throats and boils.

It has long been known to science that bacteria engaged in uninterrupted battles with each other for their lives ; they cannot bite and claw each other, nor like humans, invent means of destruction, but they attack with mysterious chemical weapons. Dr. Emmerich and Dr. Löw had found that the bacillus of green pus (Bacillus pyocyaneus) which impedes the healing of wounds, though itself a producer of disease is yet a microbe-killer. It makes a substance that destroys the microbes of cholera and diphtheria as well as the anthrax bacillus. This substance Emmerich called pyocyanase. Fleming had compared its potency with that of penicillin and had found it slight. One drop of penicillin was as effective as thirty-three drops of pyocyanase against the germ of diphtheria.

Now, with such penicillin as he could extract, he tried it on patients suffering from infections that were likely to yield to treatment with it. Of these trials he wrote : " Constant irrigation of large infected surfaces in man was not accompanied by any toxic symptoms, while irrigation of the human conjunctiva every hour for a day had no irritant effect."

But he also had to confess : " Its immediate therapeutic use was not to be.

" If the mould were grown on broth for seven to ten days the penicillin was at its maximum concentration in the fluid, but if the culture was allowed to grow for another week it was quite inert. If when it was at maximum strength it was filtered and the reaction adjusted to about pH6.8, i.e. slightly acid (the pH scale is used by scientists for measuring acidity or alkilinity, above 7 being alkiline and below 7 acid) ; then it remained active in the ice chest.

" We tried a little in clinical work, but not much. We tried it tentatively on a few old sinuses in hospital, and though the reports were favourable there was nothing miraculous. When we went to the wards and asked the surgeons if they had any septic cases we could try it on, they always said, like most surgeons in most places, I think, that they had none. Then perhaps they came along sometime afterwards and said : ' Have you got any of that stuff, I have a case I might use it on.' As likely as not, by that time the potency of penicillin had faded away. This was in 1928–1929, before any chemotherapeutic agent for the pyogenic cocci had been discovered, and before freeze-drying had been introduced into bacteriological practice.

" We were bacteriologists, not chemists, and in view of the difficulties the chemists have had in concentrating penicillin, it is not surprising that our amateur efforts at concentration were not successful."

First lysozyme, and then penicillin; twice the crescendo had risen and sounded its topmost note, but though the resolution of the theme might have been ordained in advance, it had yet to be made manifest. Meanwhile, the unemotional words of scientific reports give proof only of Fleming's unremitting persistence, of " that stubborn determination to keep at grips with the problems, often in spite of seemingly insuperable difficulties," which Mr. Chapman Pincher has noted as the hall-mark of the truly great scientist; they betray nothing of the unnumbered transports of despair as again and again the bewitched substance escaped every effort to preserve it in usable form. They hardly carry across the passage of the years the feelings of a man handling the instruments of his craft with beautiful dexterity and skill, the heat of pursuit, the range of vision and the force of the mind prising open door after door, each leading him nearer the heart of the secret he is bent on unravelling. They lift moments out of the past and hang them before our eyes as a bare, cool scene, depicting events that belong to history. Yet how could he have written otherwise? As Aldous Huxley has put it : " From pure sensation to the intuition of beauty, from pleasure and pain to love and the mystical ecstasy and death—all the things that to the human spirit are most profoundly significant, can only be experienced, not expressed. The rest is always and everywhere silence."

There can be no doubt of his certainty that he was dealing with a matter of the greatest possible moment to medicine, even though nobody hastened to pile laurels on the cradle of penicillin or garland its discoverer, and though there was a danger that so valuable a truth might totter into everlasting obscurity. " People got a bit tired of his talking about it," a colleague is reported as saying, " they thought he was over-stressing it, riding a hobby horse to death."

In 1931, two years after his discovery, he is expressing his faith in penicillin : " I have recently described a substance which has a remarkable specificity in its anti-bacterial powers.

A certain type of Penicillium, when it grows on ordinary nutrient broth, produces in the culture medium a substance which will completely inhibit, even in a dilution of one in eight hundred, some bacteria such as the staphylococci and streptococci, while even in a dilution of one in ten it has no inhibitory action on B.coli or influenza bacilli. Towards the pyogenic cocci, therefore, it is at least as inhibitory as carbolic acid, but to B.coli it is not one-twentieth as powerful. Penicillin is valuable to us at present in the isolation of certain microbes, but it is quite likely that it, or a chemical of a similar nature, will be used in the treatment of septic wounds."

In October 1932, four years after he first came upon it, he again draws attention to its therapeutic possibilities. The subject had haunted him through the years :

" In penicillin we have a perfectly inocuous fluid which is capable of inhibiting the growth of pyogenic cocci in dilutions up to 1 in 800. It has been used on a number of indolent septic wounds and has certainly appeared to be superior to dressings containing potent chemicals . . . The practical difficulty in the use of penicillin for dressings of septic wounds is the amount of trouble necessary for its preparation and the difficulty of maintaining its potency for more than a few weeks."

Over a decade and a-half later, an American was to place the credit for the use of penicillin as a therapeutic application fairly and squarely on Fleming's shoulders. " It has been said," stated Dr. Wallace E. Herrell of the Mayo Clinic, " that not very much was heard of penicillin for ten years. On the other hand I would like to point out that Fleming did use it in broth cultures in his laboratory and that although he holds fast to the fact that he is a bacteriologist primarily, he must admit that he is somewhat of a clinician because he used it to irrigate human conjuntivæ and infected wound surfaces. Therefore the prize of priority also for attempting to use it on human beings must be awarded to him."

There is nothing in the sciences of Heaven or of earth which tell of the trick of turning a bacteriologist into an expert chemist overnight. Without some such magical transformation, Fleming had neither the equipment nor the training to deal with the problems of concentrating penicillin ; they belonged no longer to the bacteriologist but to the chemist and the province of chemistry.

"It may be unfortunate," he has said, "that there was a lapse of some ten years between the time I described penicillin and the time when it was concentrated and purified to such an extent that its therapeutic properties could be even half appreciated. So far as I was concerned, the reason was quite simple ; I am a bacteriologist, not a chemist, and I was working in a bacteriological laboratory in which there was no skilled chemist." It is the complete answer. And pertinacious though he was, he was equally a realist. About this he could not delude himself. "We got no further because our amateur efforts at concentration met with little success, and because penicillin was a labile substance. When it was wanted it had frequently become inactive."

Yet, though he had for this reason been denied that sense of completion, of consummation, which comes to every scientist when the results of his investigations prove capable of some practical application, he tenaciously retained a firm, inner conviction that penicillin "would one day come into its own as a therapeutic agent."

It was a conviction based on his great knowledge of antiseptics and on his uncompromising ideas about what an antiseptic should be and what it should do. "You must look for an antiseptic," he states, "as something which has an affinity for, and enters into destructive combination with, the microbes." Next, it should not harm the leucocytes, those white cells which ingest the attacking bacteria. Lastly, great attention should be paid to the specificity of an antiseptic, that is, its relative potency to different microbes, and it should not lose its efficacy in the tissue fluids and serum. Penicillin conformed to all these requirements.

There is one more piece of evidence that Fleming, in a curiously intuitive fashion, was aware that sometime in the future his discovery of penicillin would attain an historical significance. During the course of his experiments, he found that cultures could be made on white paper placed on the culture medium. "This growth of moulds and bacteria on paper," he writes, "led me to a method of preparing mould cultures for museum purposes. A sterile disc is placed on the culture medium, and the mould spores are planted on the surface of the paper. They grow out into a typical mould colony. The paper is removed with the mould colony, sterilized by a formalin vapour, mounted on a flat glass disc, and covered with a watch glass. This makes a very beautiful museum specimen." It was a beautiful example also of his own fertility of mind, of the technical ingenuity he had always commanded so easily, now so sharp and swift after years of laboratory discipline.

By employing this method, he preserved the original culture on which he had first noticed the unique properties of penicillin, thus commemorating its discovery. "I thought the phenomenon was of sufficient interest not to discard the culture" he remarks.

The bacteriologist seldom gains or seeks the limelight ; his are long hours at the bench, his are the rewards of good pieces of work, of fresh data collected and added to the common pool. "You will find much light in medical research," Sir Almroth Wright was to say, "but few fruits. Fleming's discovery of penicillin comes after thirty years of hard, painstaking and often disappointing research." The fruits of Fleming's toil were not yet for him to gather ; his paper on penicillin created a certain interest in professional circles and was then mostly forgotten or ignored. As he himself said to the graduates of Pennsylvania University when he addressed them many years afterwards : "In your profession there is the evil of waiting for things to happen. Never neglect an extraordinary appearance or happening ; it is usually a false alarm, but it may be an important truth. Don't clutter up your minds with too much precedent." He had probably spoken from heartfelt knowledge, for though he had neither neglected an extraordinary happening nor cluttered up his mind with precedent, and had fallen upon an important truth, there still remained for him the evil of waiting.

A few lines remain to be added to the immediate history of penicillin. In 1929, the year in which Fleming's paper appeared, Professor Harold Raistrick, who occupied the chair of Biochemistry in the London School of Hygiene and Tropical

Medicine, and who had studied the habits of moulds, decided to investigate the chemical problems of penicillin which had puzzled Fleming. He collected a group of workers to undertake the task, including a bacteriologist, a mycologist, and a chemist. From the Lister Institute they obtained a culture of Fleming's organism ; he himself supplied them with one of his own cultures from St. Mary's, and from Dr. Thom, the American mycologist who correctly named Fleming's original mould, they got a *Penicillium chrsyogenum* that he had first discovered.

Fleming had made the nutrient broth he used for culturing penicillin from special organs of animals like the heart and the pancreas, but if it was going to be brewed in any quantity, it seemed that a medium less expensive and time-consuming to prepare would have to be found. Within two months Raistrick solved the problem. "The next advance," says Fleming, "was when Raistrick and his collaborators found the mould would make penicillin equally well in a simple synthetic medium containing a few salts and some glucose."

During the course of his experiments, Raistrick also isolated the yellow pigment (he named it chrysogenin), which appeared in the medium, thereby establishing that the antibacterial substance he sought was not to be found in it. He next set about isolating the penicillin itself from the medium. Fleming had attempted without success to extract it by mixing the fluid with ether, hoping that the penicillin would dissolve in it, so that when he evaporated the ether he would be left with pure penicillin. Raistrick, however, managed to find a method of extracting it in ether. But when he blew away the ether with a blast of sterilized air, he was bewildered to find that the penicillin had vanished. He tried again, adding some distilled water this time, and when the ether evaporated he was left with an active solution in the water. But penicillin had yet to be isolated in dry form.

Towards the end of 1931, Raistrick and his fellow-workers wrote in *The Biochemical Journal* that : "The investigation of the isolation and chemical nature of penicillin is being continued." Unfortunately, however, the mycologist who had been assisting them was killed in an accident and in the autumn of 1932, the bacteriologist in the team resigned his appointment to go elsewhere. "Lack of bacteriological co-operation," says Fleming, "hampered their work, and they published their results and turned to other problems."

As it happened Raistrick's method of extracting the penicillin from the medium by ether was one of the vital links which later helped the Oxford team, who were afterwards to concentrate it successfully. Meanwhile, like Fleming, he was baffled by the utter unreliability of its behaviour. "We had found out that penicillin was extremely labile and that its potency was destroyed by both acid and alkali and that when we extracted it with ether it disappeared. Such a thing was never known to a chemist before, it was unbelievable. We could do nothing in the face of it, so we dropped it and went on with our other investigations and experiments." This was Raistrick's final comment at the time.

He later realized that he had come closer to a solution than he had known, for when the ether in a little glass dish evaporated overnight, there remained a yellowish brown glaze resembling varnish. "There was no doubt," he observed, "that it was a very crude but concentrated form of penicillin, probably as strong as the first concentration of penicillin obtained by the Oxford team." However, he had had no bacteriologist to test its efficacy.

While Raistrick went down twisting, unaccountable paths and by-paths after penicillin, Dr. C. G. Paine in Sheffield, who had been a pupil of Fleming's at St. Mary's, read his account of this substance in the *British Journal of Experimental Pathology* and it stirred his curiosity. He obtained a culture of the mould from Fleming and grew it on broth, intending to try it out as a therapeutic agent. He stood astonished as his mould filtrates for no good reason yielded penicillin whose strength showed the oddest variations. However, having made up a supply, he applied the filtrate to three patients suffering from staphylococcal infections of the skin. Without result. He then decided to use it on four babies with eye infections. In two cases the condition had been brought about because they had contracted gonorrhea from their mothers at birth. Within three days both were cured. The two other cases were the result of staphylococcal infections, and one of them responded to treatment while the second proved obstinate.

The curative effect of penicillin on gonorrhea, even in the weak and unpurified form applied by Dr. Paine, was a very early indication of things in the future. Afterwards, when it had come into general therapeutic use Fleming was to say during a visit to America : " No one has asked me about a most important use of penicillin. It is effective in the treatment of certain social diseases. It makes a gonoccocus infection a trifling thing, much less than a cold in the head." Or as he put it to a friend with a flash of his mordant wit : " You catch it on Monday, you're cured on Tuesday and on Wednesday you may catch it again." Later, when it had proved itself to be the best thing not only for gonorrhea but for syphilis he remarked : " This may make it possible for our legislators to do something to eliminate social diseases. Compulsory notification and treatment fail where there is no rapid and reasonably certain method of treatment, but when this condition is fulfilled, it might be possible to introduce legislation which would be effective." In Spain he was acclaimed with every kind of honour, chiefly as the saviour of mankind from the scourge of syphilis. His car was decked with flowers and Union Jacks, and gifts which he could not very well refuse poured in. So laden was he that he had to ask the British Ambassador to testify that these really were gifts, or he would have been subject to enormous Customs duties on his return home. Holland awarded him a Victory Medal, and when he enquired what they meant by victory, they answered : " Victory over syphilis."

Meanwhile, Dr. Paine used penicillin filtrate to treat a colliery manager who had been injured in the eye while he was down in the pit. A small piece of stone penetrated his right eye and lodged itself partly behind the pupil. His eyeball and eyelids were so swollen and distorted that it seemed he might lose the sight of that eye. A swab taken from the outside of the eye gave a pure culture of pneumococci, the microbes which cause pneumonia and which could inflict grave damage if they attack the interior of the eyeball. Since they were known to be vulnerable to penicillin, the man's eye was washed out with the filtrate at regular intervals over a period of two days, and slowly the swelling went down. When another swab was taken and the culture examined, it showed that the microbes had vanished, so an operation was performed and the piece of stone removed without difficulty or fear of complications. Even the crude penicillin had been able to save his sight.

Dr. Paine had the right to be optimistic by what he had achieved, yet like Fleming himself, he had been brought sharply face to face with a single cheerless fact about penicillin; its instability. And until its unaccountable, quixotic mutations could be controlled, it could hardly be produced for general clinical purposes. "The variability of the strain of Penicillium and my transfer to a different line of work," he said, "led me to neglect further investigation of the possibilities of pencillin, an omission which, as you may well imagine, I have often regretted since."

Considering Fleming's remarkable pioneer work and the thoroughness of his enquiries, it might well have been assumed that the road ahead for others lay clear of many obstacles, yet as it turned out, even from where he left off, little progress had been made. Nevertheless, the work of Raistrick, Paine and Reid implicitly recognized his perceptive genius, his fine sense of deduction, his superb craftsmanship and his clean and simple powers of exposition. Through the austere disciplines of science, the severities of scientific terminology, he had managed to communicate to them the glow of his own intuitive belief that the phenomenon he had detected could provide an exceptional advance in the field of therapeutic medicine if only it could be forced to unburden itself of the mystery of its evasive nature.

"However," as Fleming records, "penicillin was not forgotten in the laboratory." He and his helpers continued to use it for what bacteriologists call "differential culture", that is, for isolating a microbe insensitive to it from a multitude of microbes sensitive to it. Pfeiffer's bacillus, the so-called influenza bacillus, is difficult to grow on the routine blood

agar medium ; and even on a medium most favourable to
its development, it is often overwhelmed by other organisms,
especially the streptococcus, so that the research worker
misses it. If, however, penicillin were applied to the medium,
the streptococcus, being penicillin sensitive, did not grow,
while the influenza bacillus grew unhindered and could be
isolated with ease. So excellent was this new technique
that Fleming and a colleague, Dr. Maclean, were able to
isolate the bacilli of influenza from the mouths of quite
healthy people. In his own words : " We had already
seen that sometimes if a throat-swab was rubbed on a culture
plate so that the inoculum was heavy, there appeared a pure
culture of streptococcus, but if penicillin was applied to half
the plate before incubation, on that half there were no
streptococci, but a copious growth of influenza bacilli. Here
the streptococci had completely inhibited the growth of the
influenza bacilli, and it was only when the cocci were themselves inhibited by penicillin that the influenza bacilli grew
out.

" We also used it," he says, " to improve the bacteriological
diagnosis of whooping cough by the cough-plate method.
Normally the cough-plate method showed large numbers
of cocci which made it difficult to detect the colonies of the
whooping cough bacillus, but if penicillin was incorporated
in the plate, then these cocci did not appear and the whooping
cough bacilli were much easier to recognize."

Having striven to perfect his laboratory techniques in this
way, he came to show how penicillin and a substance called
potassium tellurite could be used for differential culture,
and for the selective growth of certain microbes. " The
ease with which these substances can be used in common
bacteriological investigations," he writes, " makes them very
valuable to the bacteriologist and their properties deserve
to be more widely known. A comparison of their inhibitory
properties is likewise of considerable interest."

The bacteriologist employs certain stains to dye his microbes
for the purposes of easier recognition and examination under
the microscope. Some stain easily, others only with difficulty,
and one of the most common dyes in use is Gram's stain,

which acts on a certain group of microbes only. This group is known as Gram-positive, while those upon which it takes no effect are known as Gram-negative. Pencillin is chiefly effective against the Gram-positive variety, and potassium tellurite against the Gram-negative variety. Thus by a skilful use of both substances in combination, Fleming showed how he was able to inhibit the growth of microbes he did not wish to encumber his culture plate, leaving a good growth only of such microbes as he wanted to examine.

He also employed penicillin admirably to demonstrate bacterial antagonisms. " It is well known," he wrote, " that certain bacteria inhibit the growth of others in various ways. A mixture of two microbes A and B (A being penicillin-sensitive but antagonistic to B which is penicillin-insensitive) is spread over a culture plate and then over half the plate are spread a few drops of pencillin. The resultant culture will show a pure growth of B on the half to which the penicillin was applied and a pure culture of A on the other half. If, for example, a mixture of pneumococci and B. pyocyaneus were spread on a plate, the pneumococci inhibit the B. pyocyaneus so that the outer part of the culture is pure pneumococcus. Now the pneumococcus is inhibited by some penicillin-producing mould, so the portion round the mould colony is a pure culture of B. pyocyaneus. Between these, however, is a zone where neither microbe grows, since the inhibitory power of the pneumococcus on the B. pyocyaneus extends for a considerable distance so that even when the pneumococcal growth is stopped by the mould this inhibition is manifest for a certain distance."

Looking back on these events, Fleming has said : " We continued to grow the mould and made crude penicillin in small quantities throughout the ten years (between the time he discovered it and the time it came into general use), chiefly for the purposes of differential culture, but we got no further towards its purification. We maintained the culture and sent it on request to a large number of laboratories throughout the world, but there were no further publications other than our own, except, that of Raistrick in 1935, who confirmed my bacteriological findings. . .

" At St. Mary's I had been short of chemical help, and at the School of Hygiene Raistrick had lacked complete bacteriological co-operation.   Because of the lack of some co-ordinating standard institute, there was a gap of nearly ten years before chemists, bacteriologists and others got together at Oxford and concentrated penicillin sufficiently to show its remarkable curative properties in infective disease.   Even then facilities for development were lacking, and the information was taken to America where certain developments took place, so that America has justly reaped a large part of the reward.   Had we a central institute, where a complete team of workers could have developed penicillin this one discovery might well have paid for the institute over a large number of years, to say nothing of the suffering that might have been avoided in the ten years incubation period. . . .

"Nevertheless, I venture to suggest that in medicine we will never initiate anything by team-work.   That comes later.   There is need for a continuation of individual enterprise in research.   I was working on another project entirely when I observed the unusual effects of penicillin.   So I abandoned my first project and devoted myself to the new discovery.   Had we been working as a team, that first oddity would have been thrown away."

Thus there is the hand that lights the lamp, but other hands must keep it burning and carry it on ; the individual talent must have the fullest play but must somewhere fit into a coherent organization and then, when needed, collective action can exploit and extend what it has begun.   Fleming's call for an institution in which there could be a synthesis of scattered effort, recalls some words of Pasteur : " Take interest, I beseech you, in those sacred institutions which we designate under the expressive name of laboratories.   Demand that they be multiplied and adorned, they are the temples of wealth and of the future.   There it is that humanity grows, becomes stronger and better.   There it is it learns to read in the works of nature symbols of growth and universal harmony, whereas the works of mankind are too often those of fanaticism and destruction."

But at the time when Fleming discovered penicillin there

was small probability of institutions ; research was already under great financial handicap, and those in high quarters were too preoccupied with the depressed economic situation of the country to afford time for the consideration of other requirements. And the world stood at the beginning of one of those very phases of fanaticism and destruction which Pasteur had deplored.

Meanwhile penicillin rested ; Fleming went on to other things.

CHAPTER XIII

PENICILLIN: THE EVIL OF WAITING

IN 1673 Antony van Leeuwenhoek of Delft in Holland, a linen draper by trade, sent the first of a series of letters to the Royal Society in England describing what he had seen under his microscope; as he called them, his " little animals". His was the first pair of human eyes to detect protozoa, bacteria and bacilli. Bacteria were, " incredibly small ; nay, so small, in my sight, that I judged that even if a hundred of these very little animals lay stretched one against another, they could not reach the length of a coarse grain of sand ; and if this be true then ten hundred thousand of these living creatures could scarce equal the bulk of a coarse grain of sand." Bacilli, " had about the thickness of the last-said animalcules, but were twice as long ".

Such were the beginnings of bacteriology.

Before van Leeuwenhoek, in the first half of the 16th century. Paracelsus had written : " In Nature's battle against disease, the physician is but a helper. The business of the physician is therefore to give to Nature what she needs for her battle. Nature is the physician. . . . Every experiment with medicine is like employing a weapon which must be used according to its kind ; as a spear to thrust, a club to fell, so also each experiment. And as a club will not thrust and a spear will not fell, neither can a medicine be used than for its own remedy. Therefore it is of the highest importance to know each medicine and its powers thoroughly. To use experimental medicines requires an experienced man who discerns between the thrust and the blow, that is to say, a man who has tried and mastered the nature of each kind. The physician must be exactly acquainted with the illness before he can know with what medicine to conquer it."

The message of Paracelsus, reaching us across four centuries, might well have been composed in our own day ; it might even sit well upon the tables of every man of medicine as a reminder of certain fundamentals which, as Fleming had stated, often tend to be overlooked.

However, from Leeuwenhoek's time until the advent of Pasteur, small advance had been made in the science of bacteriology. Pasteur, in the middle of the 19th century, founded modern bacteriology, elucidating many of the principles upon which it is based, and administering vaccines in order to prevent infection. At the beginning of our own century, Sir Almroth Wright had started vaccine therapy for infections which had already established themselves in the body. A few years later, came Ehrlich, with his dreams of a "magic bullet", who discovered in Salvarsan a chemical compound for the treatment of a limited number of bacterial infections brought about by the *spirochaetes*, such as cause syphilis, yaws and relapsing fever. It was the opening phase of what he himself termed Chemotherapy. After six hundred and six experiments, he had succeeded in 'disguising' the poisonous properties of arsenic, leaving its antibacterial properties intact.

Yet the commonest microbes which afflict human beings remained untouched, for the chief reason that all the chemicals in use were more toxic to the human body cells than they were to bacteria, and that most of them had a very limited power of diffusion, though a great many, in a great many forms, were marketed. "Vast numbers of the population," Fleming has said, "are led to believe from alluring advertisements that this or that preparation will cure them of their sore throats or other infections. Quite often the only real recommendation which these substances have is illustrated by an old *Punch* drawing in which somebody was buying a cure 'because the advertisement speaks very well of it!'"

By his experiments during the First World War and afterwards, he had done more than anybody else to prove the shortcomings of these various chemicals for which much was claimed. In 1922 he had found lysozyme, and in 1928 he had found penicillin. Both are antibiotics, substances produced by living bodies which have the special property of killing or interfering with the growth of micro-organisms. In

comparing penicillin with older antiseptics, he had shown its
hostility to common infecting bacteria ; he had shown its
diffusibility, " an important property in any substance for use
as an antibacterial agent inside the body ", and he had shown
that it had no ill-effects on leucocytes. It is worth while
recalling those beautiful experiments he performed to indicate
its diffusibility and its relation to leucocytes :

" . . . penicillin is freely diffusible in agar. In this it differs
from the older antiseptics. This is brought out in a striking
manner in the following experiment.

" With a cork borer discs are cut out of an agar culture plate.
Discs of filtre-paper soaked in antiseptic are placed at the
bottom of the holes thus formed and the holes are then filled
with melted agar. The surface is then planted with staphylococci.
On incubation the staphylococcus grows over all the other
antiseptics but is inhibited through a considerable distance by
the penicillin, thus showing that penicillin is the only one of
these substances which is freely diffusible.

" I had since the war of 1914-1918 been interested in antiseptics and in 1924 I described what I think is probably the
best experiment I ever did. This showed up in a dramatic
fashion the relative activity of a chemical on bacteria and on
human leucocytes.

" Normal human blood has a strong bactericidal power on
the ordinary cocci, e.g., staphylococci and streptococci, but
this power is completely lost if the leucocytes are removed
from the blood. If defibrinated blood is infected with a small
number of staphylococci and incubated in a capillary space
—a slide-cell or a capillary tube—the cocci which survive
grow out into colonies which can easily be enumerated. But
only about 5 per cent. grow out. If however, phenol is added
to a concentration of 1 in 600 all the cocci grow out freely.
Here the phenol in a concentration which does not interfere
with bacterial growth has destroyed the leucocytes which
constitute one of our most powerful defences against infection.

" I had tested all the chemicals which were used as antibacterial agents and they all behaved the same way—in some
concentration they destroyed leucocytes and allowed bacteria
to grow.

" When I tested penicillin in the same way on staphylococcus
it was quite a different story. The crude pencillin would
completely inhibit the growth of staphylococci in a dilution
of up to 1 in 1000 when tested in human blood, but it had
no more toxic effect on the leucocytes than the original culture
medium in which the mould had been grown. . ."

Here then was penicillin, possessing just those qualities Fleming had always recognized as prerequisites in a good antiseptic, but which he had never before come across ; yet by a sombre irony it appeared to be for ever out of human reach.

"These things happened in 1928, 1929 and 1930," he said, "when there was no known chemical which was effective on the common microbes of the body, and there was general feeling of scepticism about the existence of such compounds."

So penicillin rested there for almost ten years.

Had he but known it, however, he was already the founder-elect of antibiotic therapy, which was to revolutionize medicine and surgery, and provide a specific against many common microbic infections which had hitherto escaped conquest. Fortune which had given him its gifts had on this occasion decided to keep something up the sleeve. But meanwhile the climate in the medical world underwent a change and became more propitious to the maturing of penicillin.

This happened in the mid-nineteen thirties, after a fallow period, and as Fleming has put it : " Striking advances had been made in chemotherapy, the whole atmosphere had changed. The sulphonamides had appeared and chemotherapy was in the air. No longer was it thought that chemicals would not affect ordinary septic bacteria in the body, for sulphanilamide had been shown to cure streptococcol septicaemia, meningitis and other diseases and M and B 693 was conquering pneumonia. The wonderful success of the sulfa drugs made every doctor chemotherapeutically minded, and whereas in the late twenties the quest for an effective anti-microbic drug had seemed almost hopeless, now, ten years later not only was there hope, there was certainty." It may be said that the nineteen-thirties belong to the sulfa drugs, but the nineteen-forties were to belong to penicillin and to antibiotic therapy.

Ehrlich, the founder of Chemotherapy, had spent much of his life seeking specific chemical agencies to cure diseases ; he also clarified the then imperfect comprehensions of the workings of antibacterial substances and fired the train of research into the character of numerous coal tar dyes, which he had shown possessed therapeutic properties.

From the beginning of our century, therefore, German scientists were much engrossed in these studies, supported by the I. G. Farben Industries, which had grown into a vast and elaborate organization bent on enlarging its commercial activities. Countless papers by German research workers dealing with various dyes and chemical compounds suitable for medicinal purposes appeared between 1900 and 1920, and during that period it is said that the experts of I. G. Farben synthesized some six thousand azo compounds, the name azo being derived from *azote*, the French word for nitrogen.

In 1908, a young Viennese chemist, Paul Gelmo, told in a thesis he submitted for a doctorate, how he had synthesized an unknown coal-tar derivative he called para-aminobenzene-sulphonamide, which was a white crystalline powder. It was only in 1919, however, that Gelmo's powder was found to be bactericidal *in vitro*, that is, when tested outside the body ; but when injected into animals it did not kill pneumococci. Thirteen years later, in December, 1932, two German scientists patented a red dye derived from sulphonamide which they named prontosil, and in the following year another German, Dr. Förster, announced that he had successfully treated with it a child-patient suffering from staphylococcic blood-poisoning.

Meanwhile Dr. Gerhardt Domagh, another worker in the I. G. Farben organization, began investigating the therapeutic qualities of prontosil. He injected a pure culture of streptococcus into a thousand white mice, who, left alone, would all have been dead in two or three days. But he and his helpers, with infinite care and patience, forced doses of prontosil down the throats of these infected creatures, and every one of them survived. He next repeated the experiment with rabbits, and they also lived. Still he did not publish a word about these hopeful results ; thorough and cautious, he wanted to assure himself further about the curative properties of prontosil and continued with his experiments.

Then, suddenly, compelled by desperate circumstances, he used it in the treatment of a human being, his own young daughter. She had pricked herself with a needle while knitting one day and had contracted septicaemia, set up by a streptococcal infection. It seemed probable that he had himself taken some of the microbes home from his laboratory in his clothing, and that they had infected her. Despite everything that the physicians and surgeons could do, she lay dying. Although he felt certain that prontosil could safely be used on people, there was considerable risk. At the same time Dr. Domagh knew that his child's life was despaired of, so he administered a large dose of the drug. Her recovery was complete. Nevertheless, for some years he did not tell the story of these palpitating events, and in 1935 merely wrote a short article describing his experiments with the thousand white mice. It aroused great interest among scientists all over the world, and subsequent research proved that prontosil was a specific chemotherapeutic agent against all sorts of pus-producing microbes, and that it was beneficial in cases of cerebro-spinal meningitis and gonorrhea.

" But," as Fleming said, " before announcing the merits of prontosil, the industries interested in its production perfected their preparation and covered it with patents. Fortunately for humanity, Trefouels and his colleagues in Paris demonstrated that prontosil in reality acted only after having been broken down in the organism, and that its action was entirely due to the liberation of sulphanilamide. This last, more simple, could do all that prontosil did, and it was not covered by patents."

Sulphanilamide was thus the important therapeutic factor in prontosil ; all that remained was for the chemists to produce it in quantity and it could be used widely in treating various diseases. It was a chemical which had been known for years and there were no patent rights in it, so the firms could go ahead and make it with great advantage to the community. Yet for some time the action of prontosil defied proper understanding. Concerning this Fleming wrote :

" Sulphanilamide injected intravenously into a rabbit *immediately* confers on the blood an increased bacteriostatic power. The blood taken soon after injection has greatly enhanced anti-streptococcal power, which has partly dis-appeared after five hours. A result of this kind indicates that sulphanilamide acts on bacteria without having to be changed into some other active substance in the body, for if such a change had to take place, there would be an interval after the injection when the antibacterial power of the blood would be unaltered, and only after this would it increase. For some time the mode of action of prontosil was a mystery, but a simple test of this kind would have indicated that it had to undergo some change in the body, for it is only a consider-able time after its introduction into the body that the blood shows enhanced antibacterial power."

Other misapprehensions were caused by neglecting the effect of large numbers of bacteria when laboratory trials were conducted, and he pointed out that they could have been avoided : " In the early days of the sulphonamides there was much confusion caused by a neglect of this factor, and it was often said that it was not possible to test these drugs satisfactorily *in vitro*. Actually there are no drugs easier to test *in vitro* than the sulphonamides if due attention is paid to the size of the inoculum and to one or two other details."

In 1938, the British firm of May & Baker, after six hundred and ninety-three experiments, during which chemists " took a bit off the sulphanilamide molecule here and substituted a bit there " finally produced an allied compound : M & B 693 or sulphapyridine. This could do all that sulphanilamide did. And more. It could deal with the pneumococcus which caused pneumonia. Pneumonia was a common and deadly disease, so the public were naturally excited when a curative drug was discovered. Yet for all, six hundred and ninety-three experiments had to be performed before the compound sought was discovered and this gave an idea of the insecure foundations upon which chemotherapy rested.

Writing about " The Progress of Chemotherapy ", Mr. N. Howard Jones states : " In spite of the success which attended the search for new and more effective sulphonamide compounds, the study of chemotherapy remained without a rational basis. The original prontosil and its successors had been discovered by the laborious and empirical method of synthesizing large numbers of related compounds and testing their actions in animal infections without any particular reasons for supposing that one compound would be better than another. The theoretical weakness was of more than mere academic significance, for until the mode of action of chemotherapeutic drugs was known further research must necessarily lack any clear guiding principles."

Such imprecision did not appeal to Fleming, whose approach to these problems was different, so that in speaking of the way in which penicillin had first been investigated he remarked: " It gives me pleasure to think that the merits of penicillin were disclosed as the results of *in vitro* laboratory tests, and not as with some other chemicals from testing substance after substance on animals until one was found to work."

Ehrlich's discovery of Salvarsan in 1909 and the coming of prontosil in 1935 stand as high points in the history of chemotherapy, but between them lay a period of sagging hopes and disenchantment. Moreover, neither Salvarsan nor the sulphonamides truly approximate to his conception of a *therapia magna sterilisans* which could act like a *blitz*, and at a stroke wipe out all infecting microbes. Treatment by Salvarsan was very protracted, and it had to be administered with a skilled judgment owing to its toxic effects on the body. Nevertheless, it represented a magnificent achievement in the field of medical research, and was of untold benefit to men and women. Similarly, the sulphonamides could do wonders in certain infections but were useless against others.

Had Ehrlich and his followers then misconceived the subtle and complex relationship between deadly microbes and their hosts ? Had they underestimated the power of these unseen creatures to adjust quickly to whatever new conditions might be brought about in their hosts ? Had they un-accountably neglected the wonderfully potent defences, provided for human beings by Nature ? They were German scientists, rejoicing in the belief of German science that the proud human intellect could sweep aside any barriers in its path towards those triumphs they thought nothing could deny it.

Opposite to them were Pasteur and his followers, whose

downright commonsense French notions allowed them no delusions about the supremacy of the human intellect. They kept their eyes on such natural forces as control the human organism, refused to believe that these could be changed or that they should be overlooked. The body's own defences were to them a primary consideration in the construction of a therapeutic system. As Dr. Boris Sokoloff has put it : " They hoped that in studying those antibacterial agents that exist naturally, they might be able sometime or other to discover the ideal therapeutic weapon against microbes. They never expressed the conviction—they never had any such conviction—that a magic bullet which would kill all types of microbes could ever be found or synthesized in a laboratory. Ehrlich's belief seemed to them contrary to the law of individuality, under which all living beings exist. They were more inclined to think that the various types of pathogenic bacteria might require entirely different types of antibacterial agents."

The saying goes that the heart of every Frenchman lives in his countryside ; his mind alone dwells in Paris. The first half of the aphorism might equally well be applied to Scotsmen, for in both these lands the rural dominates the urban, the chief interests are with Nature. Instinctively, therefore, Fleming's mind turned towards the organic resources at man's disposal ; there were immense latent powers in Nature which could be invoked. The splendid intellectual edifice of German science with its unbending faith in the limitless possibilities of the human mind deserved admiration and respect ; but with Wright, Fleming had worked to extend the accomplishments of the Frenchman, Pasteur, and his friend and collaborator, Metchnikov.

Having tested the new drugs, Fleming realised that once again Nature must vanquish the attacking microbes after the chemicals had stayed their prodigious multiplication within the organism. He said :

" The exact mode of action of drugs like sulphanilamide or M & B 693 is still unsettled, but it is generally accepted that the action is on the infecting bacteria and not on the host ; and that it is bacteriostatic rather than bactericidal. The chief result of the drug on the bacteria is some interference with their growth. . . . As these drugs do not actually kill the infecting bacteria, something must do it to account for the striking success which has followed their use in experimental infection of animals and in medical practice.

"That something is the natural defensive mechanism of the body which, while it might be powerless against a rapidly growing streptococcal or pneumococcal infection, can cope with the infection when the growth of the bacteria is interfered with by the drug.

"In the past too much attention has been paid to the bactericidal action of chemical antiseptics, and better results may be hoped for if workers gave more care to the bacteriostatic action, i.e. the power to inhibit the growth of bacteria.

"If the growth of the bacteria is prevented, the natural defences of the body can deal with the most virulent infection."

If then the onus of destroying the infecting microbes fell upon the body itself, the physician's business was "to give to Nature what she needs for her battle" as Paracelsus had advised. Therefore Fleming suggested that vaccine therapy and the new chemotherapy, should be used in combination :

"A fact which must be borne in mind is that the action of these new synthetic drugs is essentially bacteriostatic and therefore the actual destruction of the bacteria must be done by the natural defences of the body. It follows, therefore, that the more perfect are the defences—in other words, the higher is the degree of the immunity of the individual—the greater will be the apparent effect of the chemicals. For this reason it is theoretically advantageous to immunize the patient, so that when the infecting bacteria are inhibited by the chemical, the body may be in the best condition for their rapid destruction."

Coming after a long time of comparative quiet, the successes of the new chemotherapy, dazzling though they might be, were much magnified. But he could not be tempted to discard the old for the new, swayed by the rising tides of enthusiasm. Innate caution and a superb detachment now kept him easily balanced upon the rock of experience while the currents swinging about him bore along with them men of a different calibre. Good though these remedies were, they had their limitations ; it was as well to recognize them so as to judge matters in their true perspective :

" Seeing that the definition of an antiseptic is a chemical which will inhibit the growth of bacteria, it is remarkable that after the best part of a hundred years of study of antiseptics, the tests which are commonly quoted by the manufacturers of these chemicals relate only to their power to *kill* the bacteria, not to inhibit them. This power of killing bacteria in the conditions of these tests has little or no relation to the usefulness of antiseptics in a wound, septic or otherwise.

" It is possible that it is because of these tests that in the consideration of local antiseptics, as well as in the study of chemotherapeutic drugs, far too much attention has been paid to the bactericidal power of the chemical, and far too little to the bacteriostatic power. It would be better if, in a consideration of chemicals for use in septic wounds, the bactericidal power were neglected, and the bacteriostatic power were accepted as a criterion.

" The literature on the sulphonamide drugs is a good example of how the wells of knowledge may be muddied by attempts to show that the action of these drugs was bactericidal, when their beneficial action could easily be accounted for by a consideration of the bacteriostatic power.

" The natural defensive mechanism of the human body against the common infections is very considerable and is the most important antiseptic in contaminated wounds."

Again : "At present these chemicals have only established a reputation in the case of infections with very sensitive organisms, but if the basic principles are remembered, and the chemicals are given in sufficient amounts at the right time (germs become resistant to them) we may look forward to the scope of these drugs being greatly enlarged. There is no hope, however, of obtaining benefit in the many cases of infection by microbes which are quite insensitive to the drug. In most cases the sensitivity of the microbe can readily be tested *in vitro*, and if such tests were carried out these chemotherapeutic drugs would not be used indiscriminately and there would not be so many disappointments."

Chemotherapy was in truth one part of medicine, and it could not be treated as though it were the whole ; better therefore to integrate all the parts and make of them a greater whole. The strong and consistent desire for synthesis, which had once, after the First World War, enabled him to reconcile two opposing schools in the treatment of wounds, now urged him to reconcile the seemingly incompatible claims of immunotherapy and chemotherapy.

In June, 1938, he wrote a letter to the editor of *The British*

Medical Journal in which he advocated a combination of the two in the treatment of pneumonia :

" I have made some investigations into the action of T693 (M & B 693) and from these experiments I have come to the conclusion that chemotherapy and immunotherapy in pneumococcal infections are not competitive but complementary. I have found that T693 is incapable of killing any pneumococci in human blood from which the leucocytes have been removed ; every pneumococcus implanted will grow out, but there is a certain retardation of growth. If however the human blood has its full complement of leucocytes, then the presence of T693 in a concentration which ought to be easily attained in the body completely arrests the growth. The T693 can retard the growth of the cocci, but the natural defences have to do the killing.

" I have also found that human blood together with T693 and immune serum can deal with a much larger infection than the same blood containing *either* T693 *or* immune serum. This being so, the more immune the patient is the better will be the killing of the pneumococci, and the ultimate result will depend on whether the patient has sufficient resistance to deal with the pneumococci even after they have been in contact with the drug.

" For these reasons I suggest that the advent of T693 has made the problem of anti-pneumococcal serum of even greater importance. In the past serum therapy in pneumonia has suffered from the fact that it has never been possible to make a serum of potency sufficient to ensure with certainty that it would be able to combat a pneumococcal infection, but it would appear that with a combination of T693 and serum the latter is likely to be effective even when the potency of serum is relatively low. It is not difficult to make serums for all the types of pneumococci if one does not aim at very high grade potency. The typing of the pneumococcus is not nowadays a matter of great difficulty, nor is it beyond the powers of the younger generation of practitioners to make intravenous injections. True, it is much easier to prescribe tablets to be taken three or four times a day, but from the results I have obtained in the laboratory it seems clear that if the best is to be done for the patient then he should be immunized as well as treated by the drug.

" Hitherto I have only talked of serum as a means of immunization but we must not forget that it is possible to immunize patients actively by means of vaccines. . . . It is reasonable to assume that well within three days the patient who has received vaccine will have responded with an increase of immunity, and such an increase may well be sufficient to turn the scale when it is aided by a drug like T693.

" My object in writing this letter is to try to prevent physicians discarding immunological methods entirely in favour of chemo-therapy when theoretically it should be so much better to combine the two. . . . Let us not discard the older methods, but supplement them with the new if we are to obtain the best results in the treatment of our patients, which, after all, is our only aim and object."

About the same time he avows that : " Throughout my life my interest has been in active immunity by vaccines rather than passive immunity by serum." Active immunity can be obtained by the administration of suitable doses of an appropriate vaccine which creates its own antibodies, whereas passive immunity is conferred by the administration of an anti-bacterial serum containing ready-made anti-bodies. Moreover he shows how aware he is that medical men have been lured away by " the latest thing ", the sulfa drugs, to the neglect of almost every other form of treatment. He says, pressing for some return to a balanced view of the means of healing available to doctors :

"At the present moment vaccine therapy is, in practice, having something of a set-back, in that medical practitioners have become chemically minded because of the sensational results obtained in certain infections by sulphanilamide and its allies. These drugs have an extraordinary effect on a small number of bacteria which infect the human body and they are being used to treat all manner of bacterial infections whether or not there is any substantial evidence that there is likelihood of their being successful.

" However, it is certain that before long the limits of the new chemotherapy will be better understood. . . ."

Meanwhile he endeavours to rekindle faith in vaccine therapy by quoting some of its successes ; it has by no means become outmoded :

" One sometimes hears that in a particular case or condition, vaccine therapy has been tried and failed. It is well to remember that there is vaccine therapy and vaccine therapy, and this may be illustrated by the following cases—
" The first case was that of an American doctor practising as a specialist in diseases of the chest in one of the Western states. He had worked in our laboratories at St. Mary's for long periods before and during the war, and when he returned home he contracted severe influenza during the 1918–19 epidemic. After

recovery he suffered from typical spasmodic asthma. He tried the ordinary remedies and climatic treatment; then he had his tonsils removed in New York, and there he was treated with a vaccine made from bacteria isolated from his sputum—all without benefit.

"Here, then, was a case in which vaccine therapy had been tried and failed. Fortunately he thought he would come to London to see whether his old colleagues at St. Mary's could help. Immediately on arrival at Waterloo Station he had a severe asthmatic attack, so it could not be said that the London climate suited him. Examination of his sputum showed organisms, but nothing that seemed likely to account for his condition. The faeces were then examined, and an almost pure culture of a haemolytic enterococcus was found.

"He was treated with a vaccine of this organism in doses beginning with one-third of a million and increasing eventually to one thousand millions. Apart from an attack soon after treatment was started, he had no more asthma, and he is still free some seventeen years afterwards.

"When he was convinced that he was recovering he sent the news to a fellow practitioner in the Western states who suffered from asthma with a similar history. She travelled some 6,000 miles to have a vaccine made from the haemolytic enterococci in her stool, for she also had a great preponderance of this organism. On the boat on the way over she found another asthmatic with a similar history. He, too, had an intestine full of enterococci, and a vaccine was successful in his case also.

"These three cases happening together, all due to an enterococcal infection of the gut—a condition that is usually neglected —could not but make a lasting impression; but the moral of the tale is that in a particular case vaccine therapy was tried and had failed, and yet when it was tried again in another way it was eminently successful. This case could, I am sure, be paralleled by hundreds of others."

Fleming did not suggest that good results in the treatment of certain bacterial infections could be obtained by a combination of vaccine therepy and chemotherapy without first making exhaustive laboratory tests. Taking a mixture of blood and M & B 693, he added to it anti-pneumococcal serum, thereby proving *in vitro* that the antibacterial power of the mixture was greatly enhanced. Next, with Dr. Rogers and Dr. Maclean, he made experiments to support his contention that vaccine therapy could with advantage be used with M & B 693 in pneumococcal infections. Mice were inoculated

with a single dose of vaccine containing 25 million pneumococci.
After six days, these, together with uninoculated mice, were
infected with a virulent culture of the same pneumococcus.
A single dose of vaccine saved the animals which would
inevitably have died if treated with M & B 693 alone. When
the experiment was repeated with rabbits, one animal which
was vaccinated and then treated with the drug recovered
after a trifling illness ; another vaccinated but not given the
drug died, while yet another treated with the drug alone
suffered a serious illness.

" It would seem there is more hope in vaccine therapy,"
concluded Fleming.

But while these advances in medical science carried men
and women towards a higher degree of physical welfare,
there were aggravated symptoms of moral ailment in Europe
which seemed to lie beyond remedy. In England in
September, 1938, volunteers dug trenches and filled sandbags.
Until the reprieve of Munich caused them to cast aside
their spades with cheers of joy. But on September 3rd, 1939,
it was war, and they started picking up their rifles.

Fleming and his wife were in New York at the time. He
was there to attend the International Microbiological Congress,
but now he was obliged to return to London. He had intended
to visit the famous Mayo Clinic in Rochester, New Jersey,
but that had to be postponed. When he did ultimately
visit that institution, in July, 1945, he was a world-renowned
figure. As Dr. N. M. Keith who then welcomed him said :
" Our distinguished guest arrived in Rochester just six years
behind schedule."

However, after his arrival in London from New York in
the opening weeks of the war, he was given a district to
supervise under the Emergency Medical Scheme, and it was
his duty to visit hospitals all over the Home Counties.

For Fleming there were perhaps memories of Boulogne
of a quarter of a century before ; of the tramp of feet through
darkened streets, of wounded men lying stretcher to stretcher
along corridors, of heart-breaking spectacles, of incurable
infections. . . . For the doctors the problems were the same
as before, with the added responsibilities of treating air-raid

casualties. He recalled his experiments showing the powerlessness of chemical antiseptics as local therapeutic applications in septic wounds. He recollected how in the First World War, at a base hospital in France, he had examined a series of freshly inflicted injuries specifically treated with carbolic acid. Their bacterial content was much higher than that of injuries untreated by the antiseptic. Later he had investigated wounds surgically cleansed, treated with chemicals and then sutured. The results were essentially the same whether an antiseptic had been employed or not.

The causes of primary infection were as he had once outlined them : anaerobic bacteria normally inhabiting the intestines of men and animals, whose spores are found in soil, especially manured soil. They seldom invaded the body because the majority of them were susceptible to the action of lysosyme, although constantly inhaled as, for example, while gardening. Under war conditions, however, the soldier's clothing was covered with mud, probably manured soil, and here was a source of infection, particularly as pieces of his uniform were often planted in the wound by the missile which struck him down. Then these generally untroublesome microbes could thrive and bring about terrible diseases like gas-gangrene and tetanus.

A great many secondary infections were conveyed by other infected persons. Often the dressings in a surgical ward turned blue, indicating the spread of *B. pyocyaneus*, a pus-producing germ, but this was of small moment compared to the spread of haemolytic streptococcus, which only advertised its presence clinically by a serious complication such as a septicaemia. At the clearing stations in the First World War, only 15 per cent. of the wounds showed this organism, but after a week at base hospital, over 90 per cent. showed it. Already in 1919 Fleming and a colleague had published a paper establishing that here was a hospital infection. Moreover, it was likely to recur in the new war because no satisfactory method had been devised to prevent these microbes from gaining access to wounds in war-time hospital conditions. When floors were swept or infected blankets were shaken, they escaped into the air, where they immediately became a source of danger ; but they could be kept down by treating the floors with paraffin or spindle oil, and strict precautions were necessary.

Yet, while surgeons in the past had been reluctant to operate on wounds infected with haemolytic streptococci, because they were afraid of opening up fresh tissues to this most invasive organism lest they precipitate a generalized infection, they could now do so. " The surgeons in this war," remarked Fleming in 1940, " have a great advantage over those in the Great War in that they have at their disposal chemicals like sulphanilamide and M & B 693 which can control haemolytic streptococcal infections. This should make the surgery of septic wounds much simpler as, if sufficient of the chemical is administered to the patient so that his blood contains a concentration greater than that necessary to restrain the growth of small numbers of streptococci, it should be possible for the surgeon to operate on infected tissues without fear of spreading the streptococcal infection. Thus the advent of the sulphonamide compounds has changed the whole outlook on streptococcal infections and should enable surgical wounds to be surgically cleansed with impunity. The importance of this will readily be realised by any surgeon who had to deal with *septic* wounds at a base hospital in the Great War."

Fleming, on the other hand, was not hopeful about the application of sulphanilamide as a dressing in a septic wound; in the cavity of the wound were broken down pus cells and numbers of bacteria which would not allow the drug to exert its antibacterial effect. It was sometimes argued that this pus could be washed out and that sulphanilamide would then be effective, but sloughs remained, which could not be washed away, and which also contained broken down pus cells and many bacteria to interfere with the action of the chemical. Even if taken internally, it was unlikely that the drug could influence the infection in the sloughs or in the undrained cavity of a wound. He recommended that as an aid to sulphanilamide therapy the septic walls of wounds should be drained by using the old hypertonic saline or some other " drawing " substance, which could evoke fresh fluids from the vessels containing a full complement of antibacterial agents.

However, in recently inflicted wounds, where factors which inhibited the workings of the sulphonamides did not exist, it could be used for its valuable bacteriostatic quality.

During the two opening years of the war, Fleming often talked about war wounds to various medical bodies, and published papers on this topic which had again assumed such importance. He offered his exceptional knowledge of antiseptics and the first-hand experiences he had gained in France between 1914 and 1918. He was fifty-eight years old when the Second World War had broken out, and he was rendering great practical services in his work among the hospitals and in handing on to others the benefits of his own special wisdom.

Moreover, in the not distant future there was to come a contribution which had originated in his work, which was to set alight the public imagination and bring undreamt of relief to the wounded and the sick.

Meanwhile, in 1937, Professor H. W. Florey (now Sir Howard Florey), and Dr. E. B. Chain at the Sir William Dunn School of Pathology, Oxford, had with the help of colleagues completed their researches on the substance that Fleming had found in 1922 : lysozyme. Dr. Chain had revealed its chemical action, and his interest had been caught in substances with the same power of dissolving microbes. In his admirable book, *Miracle Drug*, Mr. David Masters* gives Dr. Chain's account of how the investigation of pencillin happened to be taken up :

> " People may think that this work on lysozyme led me to investigate Fleming's other discovery of penicillin, but that was not the case. I was searching for lytic agents with powers similar to that of lysozyme. Accordingly I began to make a big search of the literature, reading day after day and week after week to see what I could find dealing with the subject.
>
> " I did not find many lytic substances but I did find a number of papers dealing with germs which produced substances that affected other germs and stopped them from growing. Being

* All who wish to follow in detail the fascinating history of penicillin will find it in " Miracle Drug " (Eyre & Spottiswoode) 1946.

a biochemist, I said to myself : ' Here is a field of interest to a chemist '.

" It was sheer luck that I came across Fleming's paper in the *British Journal of Experimental Pathology* describing penicillin. No chemist would normally think of reading a work on pathology to assist his researches in chemistry, but here in Oxford at the School of Pathology the two subjects are combined under one roof, so they are closely linked and this direct association led me to go through the journal.

" In my further search of the literature I came upon Raistrick's paper describing how he had worked on penicillin. . . .

" I made up my mind to see what I could find out about penicillin. . . . By a lucky turn of chance I discovered that we had here on the spot, growing in the school, some cultures of the very mould, *Penicillium notatum,* which Fleming had grown at St. Mary's Hospital. . . .

" So I obtained my culture of the mould and started to work on the problem where Professor Raistrick had left off."

Together Florey and Chain planned their purely academic researches, of interest to scientists alone, having decided that they would explore the field of bacterial antagonisms. They then weighed the respective attractions of three subjects, one of which was *Pencillium notatum.*

" For a time," says Masters, " the two scientists hesitated in their first choice. The fact that penicillin obviously possessed peculiar chemical properties made a special appeal to Chain ; that the mould was known to produce an antibacterial substance influenced both men, and Florey found an added interest in the fact that penicillin was potent against the staphylococcus which caused so much human suffering.

" They were walking home one evening discussing the problem of what to start on first when, just as they were passing under a great elm at the entrance of the park, they decided to start on penicillin."

CHAPTER XIV

PALMAM QUI MERUIT FERAT

FOR TEN years, since 1928, Florey and his collaborators had worked on Fleming's lysozyme. Now, in 1938, they had decided to make a systematic enquiry into anti-bacterial substances produced by micro-organisms. Under an elm tree at Oxford, Florey and Chain had chosen penicillin for the subject of their future research ; they wanted to see whether it could be extracted so that its biochemical and biological properties could be investigated further.

The hand of destiny working in its own mysterious way had picked up an old theme which was to rise to a new crescendo and this time to burst into its pre-ordained finale. Fortune was now to hand to Fleming what it had so far kept back.

Using Fleming's culture and Raistrick's medium to produce crude penicillin, the Oxford team found it possible to concentrate it by rapid extraction at low temperature with ether and acid solution, and then prepared salts which could be dried, and in this form they were stable. Left with a viscous mass they were able to dry it when it was frozen. There remained a small pinch of brown powder.

The brown powder was the first salt of penicillin.

Having obtained a concentrated penicillin, they tested its action on various bacteria. They found that whereas the crude fluid inhibited their growth in dilutions of perhaps 1 in 200, the concentrated material could be diluted several hundred thousand times and still inhibit growth.

" They found as I had done with the crude culture fluid," says Fleming, " that while it was so powerful against bacteria, it had little destructive action on human leucocytes. It could also be injected in considerable doses into mice without showing any toxic effects. Then its therapeutic properties were tested in mice, in much the same way as the sulphonamides were tested. . . ."

On May 25th, 1940, while German armour was forcing its way towards the Channel Coast, Florey had eight white mice injected with a mortal dose of germs. He then gave four of them penicillin and used the others as controls. During the early hours of the following day the four controls died ; the four mice treated with penicillin were alive.

He then tried out the experiment on a bigger scale. Taking fifty mice, he injected twenty-five of them with a huge dose of virulent streptococci, which made their survival impossible. Twenty-five mice were left untreated and twenty-five were given penicillin at three-hourly intervals over a period of forty-five hours. With his assistant, Florey spent two nights in his laboratory to conduct this test. Within sixteen hours all the controls were dead ; twenty-four of the twenty-five mice treated with penicillin survived. It is reported that Florey picked up the telephone and said to one of his team : " It looks like a miracle."

On August 24th, 1940, the Oxford workers published a paper in *The Lancet* entitled : " Penicillin as a Chemotherapeutic Agent." They wrote : " The results are clear and show that penicillin is active *in vivo* against at least three of the organisms inhibited *in vitro*. It would seem a reasonable hope that all organisms inhibited in high dilution *in vitro* will slso be found to be dealt with *in vivo*. Penicillin does not appear to be related to any chemotherapeutic substance at present in use and is particularly remarkable for its activity against the anaerobic organisms associated with gas-gangrene."

" These preliminary experiments," observes Fleming, " made it clear that in this concentrated penicillin they had a substance much more potent against staphylococcal and streptococcal infections than anything hitherto known. Chain and Florey have stated that the enormous success of these early results made them think that the penicillin they were using must be nearly pure, but we know now that it was perhaps 1 % penicillin and 99 % impurity. . . . By 1941 the Oxford team had prepared enough to assay some trials in human cases. . . .

"If anybody from a lab. goes to a hospital and says : 'I have something that might cure a certain condition, can you give me a patient?' well, the patient he gets is someone on whom everything has been tried and who is regarded as hopeless."

Florey's first patient was a policeman, who in February, 1941, was lying in the Radcliffe Infirmary at Oxford, desperately sick of generalized septicaemia caused by two kinds of microbe, both sensitive to the action of penicillin. Twenty-four hours after the first injection the change in his condition was astonishing.

But, after continued administration, the stock of penicillin was almost exhausted.

Some was recovered from the patient's urine ; its properties were intact although it had been expelled from his body. There was every evidence that his life could be saved by penicillin : his temperature had dropped, the sores on his face and head were healing, his appetite had returned. For ten days "this forlorn case" as Florey called it, hung in the balance. But there was no more penicillin and the constable died. When they had replenished their meagre reserves, they tried it out again on a few more patients.

"The first series of cases," says Fleming, "were not the most suitable, but nevertheless it was clear that penicillin had a profound effect on some infections, notably by staphylococcus. It was found to be as little toxic to man as it had been to mice, except that some of the first injections caused a rise in temperature. Fortunately this pyrogenic substance was found to be an impurity which could be removed by further purification."

The Oxford team were able to write in *The Lancet* : " In all cases a favourable therapeutic response was obtained. Enough evidence, we consider, has now been assembled to show that penicillin is a new and effective type of chemotherapeutic agent, and possesses properties unknown in any antibacterial substance hitherto described."

Talking of Chemotherapy in relation to wound infections at the Royal Society of Medicine in April 1941, Fleming announced :

" There is another class of compound which threatens to be a serious rival to the sulphonamides. Some eleven years ago I described a substance which I named penicillin. About 1930 it was used as a dressing on a few septic wounds with favourable results, but as in peace-time septic wounds are uncommon in hospitals, and as the potency of penicillin rapidly disappeared on keeping, the therapeutic aspect of this substance was dropped, but it has been in constant use in the laboratory for the isolation of B. influenzae and B. pertussis (which causes whooping cough) from the midst of a mass of streptococci and pneumococci.

" Recently Chain and his associates at Oxford have succeeded in extracting from cultures of the mould a solid substance containing the active principle mixed with a considerable amount of pigment and other inert materials. This impure penicillin they have shown to possess remarkable curative properties in mice experimentally infected with staphylococcus, streptococcus and *Vibrion septique*.

" I obtained some of this impure penicillin from the Oxford workers and have compared its bacteriostatic powers with those of sulphathiazole and sulphapyridine. Using the staphylococcus and the streptococcus pyogenes as test microbes, weight for weight penicillin is four times as potent as sulphathiazole and about twenty times as potent as sulphapyridine. This should make it about one hundred times as powerful a bacteriostatic as sulphanilamide.

" Penicillin has an advantage over the sulphonamides in that it is not inhibited by large numbers of microbes, or by pus fluids. This impure penicillin possibly contains not more than 30 per cent. of the active principle (it turned out to be about 1 per cent. as has been said) so that one can easily see the possibilities of such a chemical if it could be identified and prepared on a large scale. The field is a very promising one but the final result awaits the discovery by the chemists of the structure of this antibacterial product manufactured in the growth of moulds and bacteria."

With the solid penicillin in his hands, Fleming had again been able to demonstrate to his own satisfaction that he had been correct in his prognostications ; his intuitive appreciation of its qualities were proving uncannily accurate, and battle-darkened skies were flecked with signs of hope as the little group at Oxford daily brought closer to realisation some of the dreams he had cherished those years before when he first made his momentous observation in a little laboratory at St. Mary's Hospital.

At that moment, however, all the penicillin in the world

lay in the refrigerators of the Sir William Dunn School of Pathology at Oxford University. Encouraged by their successes, Florey and his team were struggling to augment production, and had established a miniature-factory; they were the sole producers of penicillin. Yet the quantity they so carefully guarded was exceedingly small. And meanwhile the country was under German air bombardment and over it hung the threat of invasion. It is reported that the Oxford scientists had resolved to save at all costs the mould from which penicillin was extracted if ever German soldiers set foot in Britain. They planned to escape with it smeared on the linings of their jackets and around the insides of their inner pockets, where it would probably pass unnoticed. At such a time there was no hope of getting any firm to manufacture enough penicillin for essential clinical trials on any adequate scale. The minds of those in power were obsessed with a single thought : the salvation of the country. All its industries and its manpower were being mobilized to this end.

Florey turned to America, as yet not engaged in war.

The Rockefeller Foundation had already defrayed a proportion of the costs of research; it now financed the air journey to America of Florey and one of his collaborators, Dr. N. G. Heatley, and they took off from Lisbon for New York towards the end of June, 1951, carrying with them some of the mould. They arrived there on July 2nd and were soon in touch with Dr. Thom, the mycologist who had correctly identified Fleming's mould soon after he had made his discovery. Later they met Dr. R. D. Coghill, Chief of the Fermentation Division of the North Regional Research Laboratory of the United States Department of Agriculture at Peoria, Illinois. "Dr. Coghill," Fleming records, "has in many ways had an enormous influence in the development of penicillin production in America." Florey induced Coghill to commence the production of penicillin, some of the large pharmaceutical concerns became interested and manufacture began on a small but ever increasing scale.

Fleming recounts that a successful clinical test was probably decisive in clinching the issue, and describes a later meeting with the person who, after being given penicillin, made a miraculous recovery from what seemed a fatal illness. " I saw the first patient treated in America when I was over there in the summer of 1945," he said, " she was the wife of a teacher in one of the big universities ; she had puerperal fever and was treated with sulphonamide drugs. But she was dying. They gave her penicillin and she promptly responded and appeared to be getting out of danger. But then they had used up all the penicillin they possessed and had to stop. She relapsed, and it was a race between the manufacturer making up some more and the streptococcus trying to kill the woman. Well, the manufacturer won this time and the woman is now a perfectly healthy individual.

" That one episode convinced people who mattered that this thing was worth going on with, and they launched out on a big scale."

Or as he has also remarked : " It was brought to America and the super-team took it over. All the manufacturers joined up and they improved it enormously."

Thus much of the research work on penicillin was being done at Peoria, in brand new buildings with the most up-to-date equipment, in the Middle West of America, among fertile prairies irrigated by the Illinois River. " Nobody laughs when I say Peoria here," jokes Fleming, " but in the States everybody laughs. Peoria seems to occupy the same place over there as Wigan does over here. Peoria is right in the middle of the corn country and corn steep liquor was used to increase the yield of penicillin."

Peoria, an American town, which was a great grain market of the Mississippi Valley, whose name over there held a comic significance, became the centre of a vast humanitarian enterprise. Scientists, technicians and manufacturers flocked to it ; their letters and their telegrams and telephone calls kept its post and telegraph services fully occupied as they strove to resolve the forbidding and intricate problems involved in the production of pencillin. Here was American production know-how at its best.

But let it be remembered that Florey had unreservedly given to America the full results of the brilliant researches he and his colleagues at Oxford had carried out, the completed cycle which Fleming had begun. All Florey sought was a sufficient quantity of penicillin to undertake the extensive cliniclal trials without which the work done at Oxford would have remained unfinished.

However, it was not from America that Florey received his first supplies, but from the British firm of Kemball, Bishop.

" We were not idle in England," says Fleming, " we were getting on with it too. Of course we were very short of supplies and other vital things, tanks and so on, but we did not get on too badly, and between our production and the American, there was enough penicillin on D-day for every wounded man who wanted it. That, I admit, was largely due to the Americans. They got ahead. But of course, if it had not been for our efforts before that, not even the Americans would have had any."

He has also described graphically the efforts to produce penicillin :

" In the early days penicillin was made entirely by growing the mould, *Penicillium notatum*, on the surface of a shallow layer of culture medium, in the same way as I had prepared my crude penicillin ten years before. The mould cultures used both here and in America were descendants of the original strain which I isolated.

" To begin with, all the manufacture was done in bottles, all sorts of bottles, from milk bottles to Winchester quarts, and if you are making any quantity of penicillin that means processing thousands of bottles every day. Well, that means much labour, and they did devise a method of growing the mould in tanks. The mould does not like growing in tanks, You cannot simply put it into a tank and expect good results. It just grows on the top and you get a poor yield. It likes plenty of air, so you have to blow in air and keep the fluid moving, and you have to blow in air without microbes—that is not easy. It was difficult chemical engineering, but eventually they overcame the difficulty. This was one of the great advances made by Americans towards large-scale production, and penicillin was soon being made not in bottles of every shape and size but in thousand gallon tanks, which not only saved labour but brought down the cost of production.

"Another obvious way in which to try and improve manufacture was to get a better mould. For a long time the mould used was simply my original culture that happened by pure chance.

It was not selected in any way. It was inconceivable that this could be the best one. Large numbers of moulds of this particular species were tested. Incidentally, it is not all moulds, only one particular species of Penicillium makes penicillin in any quantity.

"They had soils sent from all over the world by soldiers but they did not get much out of this. They also hired a young woman in the laboratory to go down into the market and find anything mouldy. She was well known in the market as 'Mouldy Mary', and 'Mouldy Mary' went to the market one day and found a decaying cantaloup. She brought this back to the laboratory and they found that the mould on the cantaloup was producing a very fine yield of penicillin."

Meanwhile, at Oxford, Chain in his endeavours to speed up the production of penicillin had engaged women to help in the laboratories. These were the "Penicillin Girls" who moved about as though crossing an ice-bound surface, carrying out their tasks almost in slow-motion. They wore sterile white overalls, caps and masks, they had rubber gloves on their hands and goloshes on their feet. For the reason that penicillin was easily destroyed by airborne organisms, and they had to be painfully careful not to raise any dust. Their benches were soaked in paraffin oil and the floors were liberally daubed with spindle oil, but while dustlessness was ensured, they led a hazardous existence. Sometimes their feet slid from under them, sometimes the stools on which they sat. However, they accepted these little tribulations with good humour and laughed off their accidents.

In November, 1941, heartened by his earlier comparison of penicillin with the sulphonamides, Fleming mentioned the subject again at a discussion of the Biochemical Society. "The isolation of the pure active principle," he told his hearers there, "and its synthesis will open up a new chemotherapeutic field."

But the opportunity of employing the drug clinically did not come to him until August, 1942. Then a friend of his lay dying at St. Mary's Hospital, a man fifty-two years old who had been ill since the middle of June, and whose condition puzzled his physicians. They could not diagnose it although the symptoms suggested meningitis; he had a stiff neck, he was continually drowsy and his speech was rambling. Sulphapyridine and sulphathiazole had been tried, but his mind continued to be confused, he could not control his bodily functions and he developed a distressing hiccough which could not be stopped.

Examination of the spinal fluid had revealed no microbe which confirmed a diagnosis of meningitis, but on August 1st Fleming cultured the organisms on " sloppy " agar, a mixture of glucose and agar, and he detected colonies of a streptococcus. After further investigation, he tested the microbes against sulphathiazole and against his penicillin broth. They could withstand the sulphathiazole, but succumbed to the penicillin. One other experiment proved to him that the patient's defences were resisting the particular streptococcus he had found. On August 6th he telephoned Florey at Oxford and asked him for penicillin ; his friend was in extremity and it was his only hope.

That same day Florey took train from Oxford and walked into St. Mary's Hospital with the yellowish penicillin powder. Fleming at once began treating his friend.

It was a day full of augury, and by a strange coincidence it also happened to be his sixty-first birthday.

Summing up this experience Fleming has said :

" The first patient I ever treated with concentrated penicillin was a man in St. Mary's Hospital in London, a friend of mine. When he came to the hospital we didn't know what was the matter with him but eventually we found meningitis caused by a non-haemolytic streptococous. We used most of the sulfa drugs but the man kept getting worse and worse. For one or two mornings when I went up to see him I just wondered whether he was going to be there or whether he had gone to Heaven. I tested the sensitivity of the streptococcus to crude penicillin ; it was sensitive.

" But I had no concentrated penicillin ; in fact there was none in the world then except a little which Florey had at Oxford. Florey was good enough to supply me with, I think, his whole stock. I injected it into the patient's muscles and I tested the spinal fluid, but I found that the material wasn't getting into the spinal fluid very well. So I injected it into the spinal canal —it was the first time it was ever administered intrathecally. I didn't know whether I was going to kill the patient or not, but it seemed to be his only chance and, instead of killing him, in a week this man was practically well. It was a most dramatic recovery."

The recovery of a dying woman in America had convinced people there who mattered that penicillin was "worth going on with." Now the recovery of a dying man he had treated in London convinced Fleming that the Government should be persuaded to foster production, despite its overwhelming commitments in making the engines of war. "It seems that Providence has been kind in presenting us with this substance just at a time when it is most wanted" he has noted; "in the last war there were many soldiers whose wounds remained open for six months or more. Now we may hope that if sufficient penicillin is available, wounds will not become infected at all, or even if they do that many of them will be well inside one month." It was the thought uppermost in his mind; penicillin could perhaps save wounded men from some of the horrors he had himself watched them undergo in France during the First World War; no longer need they fall to wholesale septic infections as they had done then.

Already it had saved his friend's life. "This made a great impression on me," he says, "and I brought penicillin to the notice of the Minister of Supply (his friend the late Sir Andrew Duncan), who with characteristic energy immediately called together a meeting of scientists and manufacturers interested, and so started a Penicillin Committee, which was instrumental in stimulating British production."

One of the men who attended that first meeting, on September 25th, 1942, at which Fleming, Florey and Raistrick were present, is reported to have told the Chairman: "Perhaps you may not realise it yet, sir, but this is an historic meeting."

It was certainly that, for as Fleming has, with witty irony, put it: "You had firms who were deadly rivals in commerce sitting down at a table with one saying to the other: 'I have had trouble with this', and the other would tell him how to cure his trouble. It was a very nice friendly atmosphere."

So the production of penicillin under the auspices of the British Government was swiftly got under way as a result of Fleming's intervention, and arrangements were made for exchanges of information with American manufacturers. It was the beginning of a commendable Anglo-American endeavour which, unlike other endeavours forced upon the two countries by the exigencies of war, was directed towards saving life instead of taking it. So marked was its success that Sir John Cameron of the British Supply Mission in Washington could later (February, 1946), in addressing the staff of the Mayo Clinic, say :

" I would like, if I may, to pay a great tribute to the scientific staff of the various American pharmaceutical and chemical manufacturers. It has been my privilege these last eighteen months to be in the capital of your country, Washington, DC. It has been my privilege to meet many people responsible in 1943 and 1944 for the tremendous production of penicillin that is taking place.

" Had it not been for the wonderful co-operation of American scientists, American engineers and American young women, our British troops would not have had sufficient penicillin to take care of their needs.

" We will always be indebted to the United States for this, and also to men like Coghill in Peoria, Chester Keefer in Boston and Richards in Washington. These are probably the key men in the United States who have been responsible for the tremendous increase in the production of penicillin."

Yet here and there small but disturbing shadows were to be thrown across a harmonious scene by reports of individuals taking out patents to guard various processes they had engineered for the improved production of the drug. Speaking in New York in June, 1945, Fleming declared :

" It almost seems as if fate was kind to us. Concentrated penicillin came just when it was so badly needed in the midst of a bloody war. In wartime, production is not limited by economic considerations, and risks in manufacture were taken which in peace would have been considered unpardonable. Had it developed in peace, I have no doubt there would have been many patents taken out, and I suppose the free exchange of information between manufacturers on both sides of the Atlantic would have been impossible. As it is, I have heard rumours of patents having been taken out both in England and in America.

" When the basic information was given free to the world, it seems a pity that people here and there should seek to make capital out of what are, after all, matters of detail. But perhaps it is a necessity in our present social system.

" Fortunately I am not mixed up in this aspect of penicillin."

Looking back upon that high summer of 1942, who could not be struck by the curiosity of circumstance, the freaks of fortune, the everlasting unexpectedness of events as they broke over humans? *Per molto variare la natura e bella* : strange yet beautiful was Nature in her infinite variations. Fleming was being moved into the centre of the stage to play the leading figure in the end-scenes of a tremendous drama of which he had been the author. It was a part for which, unknown to himself, he had long been cast ; he had hardly anticipated it as he kept watching from the wings.

The last remaining spaces in the baffling mosaic spun by the Fates in their own good time were swiftly filling ; its message was at last growing clear.

On August 26th, 1942, *The Times* in its own aloof fashion devoted a leading article to the subject of penicillin, drawing from Sir Almroth Wright, Fleming's master, an immediate rejoinder. His letter to that newspaper was published in its columns the very next day, August 27th, 1942. He had written :

> Sir,
> In the leading article on penicillin in your issue yesterday, you refrained from putting the laurel wreath for this discovery round anybody's brow. I would, with your permission, supplement your article by pointing out that, on the principle *palman qui meruit ferat*, it should be decreed to Professor Alexander Fleming of this research laboratory. For he is the discoverer of penicillin and was the author also of the original suggestion that this substance might prove to have important applications in medicine.
>
> I am, Sir,
Yours faithfully,
ALMROTH E. WRIGHT.
>
> Inoculation Department,
>   St. Mary's Hospital,
>   Paddington, London, W.2.

CHAPTER XV

A WHOLE NEW WORLD OF SCIENCE

Palman qui meruit ferat ! Fleming was now being mentioned in the same breath as Lister, Koch, Ehrlich, Jenner and the other benefactors of humanity, and modern communications and modern methods of publicity were sweeping his name into all the quarters of the earth. " Happy is he who already belongs to history in his own lifetime," said Lord Moran, speaking of him.

But he continued to work in his laboratory as forces gathered to lift him to eminence. He conducted *in vitro* tests of penicillin and published his conclusions in *The Lancet*, and commanding the substantial experience of the years and the brilliant ingenuity which was a special gift, he suggested technical improvements for various tests with the drug. With some surprise he listened to the telephone ringing with increasing frequency, daily faced a larger pile of letters, and was called upon to attend meetings of all kinds. His appointment book filled up with disconcerting rapidity. Such interruptions of the habitual quiet within his laboratory, such demands upon his time he now had to be prepared to face. But they did not altogether appeal to him.

" I am a simple bacteriologist," he once said to a gathering of distinguished listeners, He had meant it.

It was wartime ; all the supplies of penicillin available were set aside for serving men and women, and as yet civilians could have none. Moreover, though its production had high priority both in Britain and in the United States, there had to be conservation for use when the invasion of Europe took place.

" Penicillin has had, perhaps, a romantic career," Fleming has written. " Born in times of peace by a stray mould-spore implanting itself on a microbic culture where it was not wanted, it reached maturity at the height of the greatest of all wars, when it was there to help the wounded soldier, and do its part in preventing the awful miseries resulting from septic infections such as were seen in the last and in all past wars."

In fact this aspect of the history of penicillin can be traced back to those early bleak days when the Oxford workers were its sole producers, and were struggling to increase its manufacture. With considerable vision, Florey realized that the needs of the wounded had to be set above all else for the time being, so in June 1942 he gave some of his precious reserves for the experimental treatment of burned airmen of the R.A.F., and was gratified to learn that they had benefited.

In July 1942 he sent a small amount of penicillin out to Cairo, and received favourable reports of it after its use on men wounded in the desert fighting. In May of the year following, proper clinical trials began in Algiers, under horrifying, fly-infested conditions. Soon he arrived there himself to participate in them, and for three months he worked with army doctors to perfect the techniques of its administration. Before he left Algiers he had set down the foundations of penicillin treatment in war wounds. It had sometimes meant overturning well-established surgical practice, and his suggestions often unnerved surgeons who did not possess his profound knowledge of what the new drug could and could not do.

" I remember one young medical officer," he is reported as saying, "looking over my shoulder as I indicated to the surgeon what I wanted him to do. 'It's murder, it's murder', the voice kept repeating in my ear. It was not pleasant but the patient recovered."

The picture had startlingly changed since the days of 1914–1918 when Fleming and his colleagues had accomplished so much for wounded men. Now penicillin could be injected into the veins, the muscles or under the skin and, when absorbed, it reached the microbes through the blood stream ; it could be injected into the infected part or used as a local application ; sometimes systemic and local treatment could be combined and a variety of infections were quickly disposed of. Even the frightening gas-gangrene could be dealt with hopefully, gonorrhea vanished and syphilis could be made to yield. " The most dramatic results of systemic penicillin treatment," observed Fleming, " are perhaps obtained in gonococcal infections. In the Forces, especially the American Forces, this disease has been treated extensively." Questioned by an American journalist about a ' one-shot cure ' for gonorrhea, he smiled and replied quietly : " Well, let's say a two-shot cure is certain."

The trials begun in North Africa were continued in Sicily. Quickly penicillin was saving hundreds of cases which would otherwise have gone down in the records as fatal casualties, and it was cutting down to about half the duration of the wounded man's stay in hospital.

In particular it was used prophylactically ; the soldier received it as soon as possible after wounding and continued to receive it during the whole course of his transit from the front to a base hospital where he could be properly cared for by a surgeon. Injuries could be sewn up quickly so as to avoid contamination without the old fear that microbes lodging in them would generalize themselves and bring about septicæmia.

" The surgeons are unanimous that there has been a very great diminution of sepsis and of gas-gangrene," Fleming wrote with satisfaction, no doubt making mental comparisons with all he had seen in France during the First World War.

Given systemically before an operation in a large dose, it assured that the blood would be strongly bactericidal during the operation and for some time afterwards, and it was invaluable in wounds involving the face and limbs. Wounds involving compound fractures of the femur could often be sewn up and firm union occurred within six weeks.

" What a change from the last war ! " exclaimed Fleming, reviewing these incredible advances.

When the landings in Normandy took place and fighting began, exciting accounts of penicillin came back from all sides. Lord Moran, according to one report, stated that 95 % of the men who had been treated with it since the landings had recovered. A doctor from the battlefront said : " Infection of wounds is being kept to a minimum owing to the liberal use of penicillin. We have lots of it here. Tell people at home not to complain if they can't get it, because it is saving many lives on this side. Deaths from gas-gangrene are only a third of what they were in the last war. One seriously wounded man had £10,000 worth of penicillin and is alive to-day because of it. It is indeed the wonder drug of the century." An American source held that 18% of American soldiers who contracted pneumonia in the First World War died; in this one the mortality rate had been seven-tenths of 1%.

Subsequent figures, perhaps more reliable, tell how the Royal Army Medical Corps dealt with about five million casualties during the whole war. More than half the stomach wounds healed; only 20% of shattered limbs were amputated as against 70% in the First World War; similarly, loss of sight had dropped from 67% to 37%.

But no dry statistics could possibly bring to the imagination the measureless achievements of penicillin in war, could help to re-enact the events which took place in the tented field-hospitals among Norman apple orchards, in base hospitals, and as the battle swept onwards, among other changing scenes in France, in the Low Countries and in Germany itself.

Summing up in his Report on Operations in North West Europe from June 6th, 1944, to May 5th, 1945, Viscount Montgomery of Alamein writes : " The healing of war wounds has been revolutionized by the use of penicillin. Many men who in the last war would have been permanent invalids were fit and ready to go back to the line within a month of being wounded."

When visiting the Walter Reed Hospital in America soon after the peace, an officer in Fleming's presence asked a group of men how many had been treated with penicillin. Every hand went up. A sergeant who had received it for a jungle disease contracted in the Netherlands East Indies cried : " There's your answer, doctor, thank you." At the same hospital Fleming was told how two army doctors there had been administering penicillin with peanut oil and beeswax so that the body should retain it longer. " Maybe we didn't follow the instructions right," he answered cheerfully, " we just mix it with water in England."

Penicillin flared up into news, it topped even the high dramas of the biggest conflict in history, pushed medal-winning heroes into comparative obscurity and kept the headlines ; Fleming's tranquil existence was invaded by curious pressmen who insisted upon details both personal and scientific. With calm and good-nature he obliged them. Colourful tags and labels were quickly attached to penicillin ; chiefly it came out as the " wonder drug " or the " miracle drug ". " People for the most part have called penicillin a miracle," Fleming had said, " for once as a scientist I agree. It will save thousands of lives." From him, however, this was a plain statement of fact.

Rumours of fabulous production costs was an attractive topic and again Fleming gave a plain answer : " The original cost of production was enormous, but the need for saving the lives of wounded men made cost no object and enabled science to overcome this initial obstacle."

Some of the ensuing results were amusing. A highly reputable journalist on an equally highly reputable national daily managed to make him tall and thin ; in a lesser journal, the caption under a picture of a man looking remarkably like a Prussian general read : " Sir A. Fleming " ; yet another paper told how he spoke with an Oxford drawl !

Once a report got put about that, some fifty years ago a young London boy on a visit to Scotland was saved from drowning by a farm boy. The rescued boy's parent provided the money for the farm lad to study medicine. In 1943 penicillin was flown to the Middle East for a statesman seriously ill with pneumonia. Churchill was the rescued boy and statesman, Fleming was the farm lad ! "

The story, which had apparently gained currency before, raised the usual questions from newspapers. " My husband laughed about it at the time," Lady Fleming told them, " I expect he will again." As one account later pointed out shrewdly : " Mr. Churchill was fourteen when Sir Alexander Fleming was seven ! "

Fleming sighed for the old tranquility again. " There are so many people asking questions that I can't get any work done ; it's a little embarrassing." But he was still too newsworthy to be left undisturbed.

" The modest scientist," said a correspondent, " is not at all happy about the world-wide publicity he receives, nor about the exaggerated claims made for the ' wonder drug '. He feels strongly that it is cruel to raise false hopes among sufferers with certain diseases." Patient though he was, Fleming was distressed by this aspect of newspaper publicity, so that on one occasion he lost his habitual reserve and protested : " I never did say penicillin was a cure-all, the newspapers did that. It was not a medical publication which credited penicillin with curing everything under the sun. It has an extraordinary effect on many of the common diseases, but on others it is quite inactive.

" The publicity given it has caused me to receive thousands of letters from sufferers from tuberculosis and many other ailments. The saddest thing I have to do is to answer letters asking if it will cure this or that or the other dread disease."

Still, there were authentic stories too. The late Mr. Phillip Guedalla, the author, speaking at the Royal Society of Arts in June 1944, told one about himself :

> " I am one of the animals into which the life-saving substance has been injected. I am afraid that in my case it was applied as a corpse-reviver at a very late stage, but it revived the corpse. If it had not been for the investigation which Professor Fleming carried out so brilliantly, I should not have been here this afternoon. I wish to testify with all humility and thankfulness to the treatment which in six weeks can bring a man out of the shadow into a state in which he is able to resist the efforts of three Government departments to amend the text of his book."

For some weeks in the summer of 1943, all America was held fascinated by endeavours to save the life of a little girl, two years old, by penicillin treatment. On August 12th, at twenty to four in the afternoon, " a little white light flashed a summons on the *New York Journal-American* city desk switchboard." The city editor who answered the telephone (according to an account in that newspaper), heard these words :

> " ' Hello, is this the city editor ? '
> " ' My little girl is in the Lutheran Hospital. The doctors say she has only seven hours to live—unless she gets the new drug penicillin.
> " ' It is her only hope. The doctors have used sulfa drugs and everything else. I must find someone with enough to help her.
> " ' Can you help me ? ' "

The caller identified himself as Mr. Malone, and his small daughter's name was Patricia. From this moment on, the diary of events makes something like a " thriller " :

3.45 p.m.   *Journal-American* city editor calls the office of Surgeon General Parran in Washington to obtain release of the drug.

3.47 p.m.   Reporters canvass drug companies in the city of New York to locate supplies. Penicillin had hitherto never been released for civilian use. Therefore it was found not to be stocked by druggists.

3.50 p.m.   *Journal-American* calls Dr. A. N. Richards, chairman of medical research of the Office of Scientific Development in Washington. He immediately offers aid.

3.52 p.m.   Dr. Chester Keefer, of Boston, the only man in the country empowered to release the drug for civilian use, is contacted at his office. He too promises co-operation.

4.0 p.m.   Dr. Keefer acts immediately, calls Dr. Collitti, staff physician at the Lutheran Hospital.

4.10 p.m.   Dr. Collitti receives call from Dr. Richards in Washington saying the drug will be released.

4.15 p.m.   Dr. Richards tells the *Journal-American* that he has conferred by 'phone with Dr. Keefer. A telegram has been despatched to the Squibb Laboratory in New Brunswick, ordering the drug to be released.

4.20 p.m.   Dr. Keefer again contacted, transferred by the *Journal-American* switchboard to Squibb Laboratory, New Brunswick, and the drug is released by telephone. But it must be got to New York.

5.15 p.m.   Police escort asked for to speed delivery of the drug. The request is granted by the Commissioner of Police.

6.30 p.m.   Dr. Collitti met by *Journal-American* reporters in a car, raced to New Brunswick.

7.30 p.m.   After an hour's swift ride, Dr. Collitti picks up the drug, signs for it and begins return journey.

7.45 p.m.   Returning car is picked up by police escort, rushed back to New York.

8.38 p.m.   Dr. Collitti arrives back at the hospital.

9.10 p.m.   Dr. Collitti administers the penicillin to Patricia.

Patricia Malone was suffering from a somewhat rare malady, diagnosed as *Acute Staphylococcus Albus Septicæmia*. The child was " in delirium " says the medical report, " the tissues were livid, the respirations were shallow and rapid, the pulse rapid and thready. Penicillin treatment was instituted by continuous intravenous drip. At the end of 48 hours the change in the condition of the child was dramatic. The child was mentally alert, the colour was good, nourishment by mouth was given and retained. The course of the illness was stormy . . . "

About six weeks later she went back home to her parents, well again.

However, despite a few exceptions, the use of penicillin for civilians came under severe restriction during the war. Yet the experiences gained in its administration to the war-wounded provided a firm basis for its employment in general civilian practice when the peace came, and much progress was made which was of future advantage.

Fleming was careful to point out that penicillin was not the " magic bullet " which had gripped Ehrlich's mind, it was not a *therapia magna sterilisans*. He stated :

" The newest and most successful antiseptics, the sulphona-mides and penicillin are very specific ; they affect certain microbes and have no action on others. It seems little likely that there is a hope of getting an antiseptic which will affect all microbes without being poisonous to the human cells. We shall have to content ourselves with a series of these which will cover the whole range of microbic growth.

" This will make it more difficult for the doctor. There is no doubt he would like to have one chemical which he could use for every infection, but if that is impossible he must content himself with chemicals which affect only some, and he must learn which they affect and not waste his and the patient's time by using the wrong chemicals for the wrong microbes.

" It will mean, of course, that he will have to pay more attention to bacteriology than heretofore. . . .

" Penicillin was born in the laboratory and has grown in close association with the laboratory. Penicillin treatment can only be satisfactorily carried out with a bacteriological laboratory. . . .

" I do not mean that in all cases penicillin should be withheld until the bacteriology has been investigated. In years gone by, for example, the surgeon did not worry much about the nature of the infection. If, for instance, he encountered a septic wound, he applied a non-specific chemical and did not care very much whether the infection was one by staphylococci, streptococci or *B.coli*. The advent of specific drugs has, however, made it necessary—if he wished to do his best for his patient—to take more interest in the infecting microbe.

"Now surgeons feel happier when operating under a ' penicillin umbrella ', and I have been told by my surgical colleagues that many operations are undertaken with a light heart in cases where a surgeon would not have dared to interfere in pre-penicillin days.

"But I want to emphasize that penicillin is not a substitute for effective surgery, especially in dealing with wounds. . . .

"In penicillin we have an antibacterial substance important to bacteriologists because of the marked specificity of its bacteriostatic power, and still more to the clinician because of its extraordinary curative properties in some of the common infections. But to succeed in treatment, it must be brought into contact with the microbes either locally or through the blood. (Just get the champion into the ring with his opponent and he will do the rest).

"If this is forgotten, or if it is used on insensitive infections, nothing but disappointment could result. But properly used in the right infections, results will be obtained which cannot be approached by anything else.

"I would hate to say that I have used penicillin treatment on a carbuncle if I had merely spread some cream on the surface. That is using penicillin but it is not penicillin treatment."

Whenever he was called upon to talk about the drug, he dwelt not so much upon its marvels as upon its limitations, and he returned to familiar themes. As with the sulphonamides, the actual destruction of the infecting bacteria had to be done by the body cells. Furthermore, misguided use of penicillin could have unhappy consequences, microbes grew penicillin-resistant. As he explained : " It is a perfectly non-poisonous substance, but although you cannot poison yourself with it, you can do harm not by taking too much but by taking too little. Suppose you exposed a microbe to a non-lethal concentration of penicillin, what happens is that the microbe educates itself to resist penicillin. These microbes are living organisms and they adapt themselves.

"Suppose you take an example : one of you has a sore throat ; you say : ' Now we will take this penicillin ', and you spray your throat for a little while, enough to take away the pain and the irritation, and you think, ' this is fine '. But you have not killed the microbes, all you have done is perhaps to educate them. You have still got microbes in your throat, and when you are talking to your best girl you pass them on to her. She perhaps gets not a sore throat but pneumonia. Then she is treated with penicillin and she dies. Well, who is responsible for killing her ? " It was certainly a nice point in ethics, nicely made.

He had other stories to tell about the unenlightened administration of penicillin. " Systemic treatment is easy," he said, " but there remains a good deal of ignorance. I was told the other day by a colleague that he called on a physician when the telephone rang. He could not help hearing one side of the conversation ; it went on until the physician said : 'And how do you give this penicillin ? Is it three times a day after meals ? "

" I heard another true story of a distinguished London surgeon who had been called upon to open a whitlow. After the operation the practitioner asked him whether he would like the patient to have penicillin. He replied : ' All right, give him some penicillin lozenges to suck '. Another shameful misuse of a good drug."

What then is penicillin ? Who better than Fleming himself to give the answer : " It is a perfectly white compound and it is extraordinarily powerful. You can dilute it about fifty million times. That is an enormous dilution. It is very difficult to imagine what a fifty million dilution is, but suppose you translate it into something concrete. We did a bit of arithmetic on this some time ago, and we came to the conclusion that one drop of water diluted fifty million times would fill a little more than 6,000 whisky bottles ! "

Referring to the chemical formula of penicillin, he explained : " It includes a previously unknown natural combination—the four-membered B.lactam ring. It is this ring which makes penicillin unstable, and treatment with almost all strong reagents breaks this ring and renders the penicillin inert. Strong acids and alkilis destroy it as do many metals, especially copper. This last is important in some ways. For instance, there was one inhaler designed for penicillin which had a copper container. We found that when penicillin solution was sprayed from this, the vapour was reduced in potency to about one-fifth of what it should have been."

And for those with a taste for formulæ, that for penicillin is :

$$CH_3—C(CH_3)—CH.COOH$$

$$\begin{array}{c} CH_3 \\ | \\ CH_3—C—CH.COOH \\ | \quad\quad | \\ S \quad\quad N \\ \diagdown \quad \diagup \\ CH \quad CO \\ \diagdown \quad \diagup \\ CH_1 \\ | \\ NH.\,CO.\,R \end{array}$$

Penicillin was in truth completing the work begun by Lister. Lister prevented microbes from gaining access to a wound by using carbolic acid, and thus changed the face of surgery, for this permitted the surgeon to sew up an operation wound with the knowledge that it would not suppurate. There used to be a phrase, ' laudable pus ', and it used to be taken as a sign that the patient would recover, but to-day pus of any kind, laudable or otherwise, was a reflection on the surgeon's method.

The new chemotherapeutic drugs, the sulphonamides, and especially penicillin, were rounding off Lister's efforts by destroying septic microbes *after* they had established themselves in the body.

" Penicillin," said Fleming modestly, " may be making some small revolution in surgery, but another revolution of the magnitude of Lister's is impossible. Still, a minor revolution is something, and I am glad to have had some part in it."

But he was being too modest, for the coming of penicillin was more, it was a major revolution in curative medicine, as radical in its consequences as the coming of nuclear physics has been in quite other directions. It placed in the doctor's black bag a weapon against many microbes as advanced as the atomic bomb.

Moreover, its discovery gave a world-wide stimulus to research and acquainted medical men with other antibiotics. Streptomycin may well turn out to be a cure for early tuberculous infections and thus bring about the disappearance of sanatoria in time to come, and the names of substances like aureomycin and chloromycetin and still other biotics, now on everybody's lips, might never have been heard of if Fleming had not one day seen staphylococci dissolving on a mould-spotted culture plate. " Fleming, like Pasteur, has opened up a whole new world of science." Such was the verdict of Thomas Parran, Surgeon-General of the United States Forces.

And how well Fleming with his deeply intuitive mind realized this special implication, for even in the early days when penicillin had not come into general use he was saying : "The greatest benefit penicillin has conferred is not the drug itself but the fact that its discovery has stimulated new research to find something better."

_____

POSTSCRIPTS :

(1) " Dr. Fleming's critics say his discovery came about by accident. Just remember that when Wellington waited for Blücher to come with help to Waterloo, Blücher was lost until he met a young Belgian boy who showed him the way. That was by accident too. May the world be saved by more such accidents." (Senator Barkley of Kentucky.)

(2) " Discoveries of the first magnitude are rare, and for them Dame Fortune often plays a part in arranging the pieces on the board so that the answer is clear to one particular worker whose thoughts run in the right direction. The researcher might remember these lines from Kipling's ' Explorer ' : ' God took care to hide that country till He judged his people ready ; then he chose me for his whisper and I've found it and it's yours.' " (Sir Alexander Fleming.)

(3) ". . . then there is penicillin, which has broken upon the world just at the moment when human beings are being gashed and torn and poisoned by wounds on the field of war in enormous numbers, and when so many other diseases hitherto insoluble cry for treatment. . . . (The Prime Minister, The Rt. Hon. Winston S. Churchill.)

(4) " I feel like a man singing at my own graveside. The general use of penicillin is going to deprive us of a great deal of our surgical work. I see wiped out at one stroke a lot of the operations I have been performing. There will be no more

carbuncles, boils, childbed fever and septic pneumonia. Pneumonia will be handled so easily in future that there will be no chance of complications. The social diseases which have exercised the minds of politicians so much will be a problem no longer.

" I think Sir Alexander Fleming will have done more people out of a job than any other person at any time." (Mr. Dickson Wright, surgeon, addressing a Congress of the Society of Physiotherapy in London.)

POST-POSTSCRIPT :

Mrs. Eva Wood of Bungay, Suffolk, is a little scornful of this wonder drug that has been discovered from mould called penicillin. Her great grandmother used to collect all the new copper pennies she could, and old copper kettles, smear them with lard and leave them in a damp place. When the mould had formed she would scrape it off into little boxes and everybody for miles around came to her for the remedy for whatever ailed them.

CHAPTER XVI

THE LIGHT OF RENOWN

"THE RESUSCITATION of penicillin as a chemotherapeutic remedy is due to the brilliant work of Florey and his colleagues at Oxford," Fleming has said. "The success of the Oxford workers is a great argument for team-work in a detailed investigation of this sort. Whether team-work is an advantage for the initiation of something new is quite another matter." He had frequently expressed his passionate belief in the individual. Although in a growingly complicated world the initiator of a project was less able to carry it through to a successful end without the help of others, nevertheless from the individual stemmed the idea which gave impetus to the group.

It was a view he dared to proclaim even in Detroit, that legendary city of mass-production. "You Americans," he declared, "talk too much about team play. If I had belonged to one of these teams I would never have found penicillin. I am glad to say this in Detroit where all I hear is mass-production, team-work and organization, and very little about the individual."

He was thinking, no doubt, of those endless hours in his laboratory when, with all his patience and tenacity stretched to painful limits, he did his experiments again and again, scrapping them, repeating them, until they were perfectly executed. He had been alone, And always there was his astonishing capacity for recording minute detail, data which was ultimately synthesized into a coherent pattern.

But nothing hung on the wind any longer. Destiny had spoken out, and Fleming who had lived silently, within the companionship of his inmost thoughts, was called upon to savour the variegations of a more temporal existence. Yet as destiny had always seen it the end was implicit in the beginning, already guaranteed by the qualities inherent within him.

"He is a man of brilliant and original mind, he is most valuable." Sir Almroth Wright had said that of him.

The very qualities which had served him well were to go on serving him well now that he walked in more public ambits, unimpaired by success : his caution, his modesty, his piercing intuition, his level head, his unfaltering loyalty, which comprised the impregnable structure of his character.

At the Savoy Chapel Royal in June 1944 he said : " The late Sir Ronald Ross has enshrined in memorable poetry the joy that comes to a scientist who alleviates the pain of suffering humanity." An achievement of such profit to the world as his own stood fully recompensed by this alone. By comparison the plaudits, the honours that flowed thick and fast were of lesser substance. But he would have been less than human had he not been gratified, had he not felt the warmth of acclamation, the sense of consummation they brought. At the same time he had always regarded ambition and success circumspectly. Had he not warned : "Ambitions have a way of growing, one success breeding the desire for another ? " It was reminiscent of Ehrlich who had once written : " He who worships success can make the world neither good nor happy." And what was success to Fleming ? " You're looking over the edge at the Jordan one day and you're on dry land the next." Success, moreover, had remarkable variety. The morning mail could bring an unusual and touching letter about the aspirations of a young boy from a fellow-scientist in America :

Dear Dr. Fleming,
    Several months ago I had a young visitor who was so interested in bacteriology that I fitted out a small lab. for his own use. I had almost forgotten him when I received a copy of his high-school paper, which is enclosed.
    I had given him a culture of penicillin, a direct descendant of your culture by the way. I know you are a busy man, but if you could just drop him a line saying that a copy of his school paper has come to hand, such a letter would raise him and his school to the scientific stratosphere. He is fourteen years old, a smart chap and intensely interested in bacteriology.
    I hate to bother you, but feel this is purely missionary work.

The morning mail could also bring an invitation to dine with a crowned head :

D'après les désirs de Son Altesse Royale, le Maître des Céré-
monies de la Cour a l'honneur d'inviter Sir Alexander Fleming
. . .

Yet life had not been without its hazards and its inconveni-
ences. Like many of his fellow-citizens in London, he and his
family had had a lucky escape during the *blitz*. A landmine
which destroyed the beautiful Chelsea Old Church had rendered his home uninhabitable, and it had been a near thing,
especially for his son, since a falling beam barely missed him
as it crashed down. So after living within a stone's throw of
Whistler's house for years, and of the reaches of the Thames
he had painted, Fleming and his family were forced to move
to a furnished place in Highgate. Meanwhile their Chelsea
house was hit again, this time by an incendiary bomb, which
set the top floor alight. They were appalled to find the things
they had left behind ruined by the water the firemen had had
to pour on the blaze.

In October 1943 he said in a letter to a friend : " We cannot
expect much now as there is no labour available for anything
but comparatively small jobs, but one day things may come
right and in any case there is hope." It was not till June 1944
that repairs to his damaged home began. " They are starting
work on our old flat so perhaps before long we will be back in
Chelsea." Even his house at Barton Mills had suffered, but
nothing much could be done about that until 1951. In March
of that year he remarks to a friend : " I had to come here to
get things in order. It has not got straight since the war and
there are all sorts of things to be done to the house and the
garden to repair the war damage." While the restoration was
being carried out, he installed a laboratory there so that he
could work peacefully during his leisure in the tranquility of
the Suffolk countryside.

In 1943, at the age of sixty-two, Fleming was elected a
Fellow of the Royal Society, that institution founded in 1660,
to whose members Newton's *Principia* and van Leeuwenhoek's
papers had been read. Forty-one years before he had won his
scholarship to St. Mary's Hospital, beginning his career among
a remarkable company of young men, one of whom was to
become President of the Royal College of Physicians, five of

whom were to become professors and two Fellows of the Royal Society. One was to receive a barony and two were to receive knighthoods.

It was a famous occasion and the hospital made a presentation to him. In a letter dated October 5th, 1943, he wrote to Ronald Gray saying : " They had their meeting at the hospital and presented me with a very beautiful silver salver. That was pleasant, but it was not so nice to have to sit on a platform and then have to make a speech. I hope I did not disgrace myself, but in that matter I am not a good judge." He need not have had any qualms. His unaffected and conversational style was, as always, very effective. He continued : " The papers seem to have been busy with penicillin. I actually had a request from somebody in America for an autograph, and I had a letter of congratulation from the council of my native village, Darvel. The provost of the town had read about penicillin when he was in Cairo. On Thursday week I am supposed to be broadcasting to Sweden—at least, what I am going to say is to be translated into Swedish and transmitted. They want me to go down and speak a few words in English as an introduction . . . "

During this account of a full programme, he remarks : " Nothing startling happening here. We all just go on." As usual, work remains the centre of his life, the manifestations of success have their place on the periphery.

In June 1944 it was announced that he had been knighted, and in the month following *The Times* carried this formal paragraph : " His Majesty the King held an investiture at Buckingham Palace and conferred the honour of knighthood on thirty-eight gentlemen. Among those who received the accolade was Professor Alexander Fleming." "The Lord knows what my new form of address is," he had written to Ronald Gray " . . . it will be simply Sir Alexander, I suppose."

Seats of learning everywhere in the world hastened to confer their distinctions upon him. The sombre academic fusc was splashed with crimsons, violets, purples and blues as he passed through Gothic portals, Renaissance quadrangles and plain red-brick doorways to mount the platform and, amid impressive ceremonies often rooted in the ancient past, to add new degrees to old. A brief entry in *Who's Who* sums them up by describing him as "*doctor honoris causa* of many universities in Europe and America." At the Royal Society of Medicine he shared the platform with Florey, and each of them received an ovation the like of which had not before been heard from the usually restrained members sitting in august assembly.

In June 1945 he went to America and Canada. "I want to see how the baby's growing up," he told them, referring to penicillin. They found him "an easy, personable, smiling man, with none of the austerity frequently ascribed to scientific geniuses, and with an impressive simplicity that belied the numerous citations and awards conferred on him."

"Did you fly?" they questioned, and to this he replied: "Why, when there is no need? If you go too fast you die too young and I don't want to die too young." They asked him whether he intended visiting the West Coast. "God made America too big," he told them, "and three days on a train are not like three days on a boat." He was winning points, and they were taking to him.

Everywhere reporters crowded in on him, people tried to tell him how to use the drug he had discovered, they shook his hand until they almost wrenched it off, and backslappers, eager to tell their friends they had met him, managed to overcome their awe of his title and his eminence. With the flash-bulbs exploding and the cameras trained on him, he remained patient and friendly, even taking the trouble to explain that the correct pronunciation of penicillin required the accent on the second i. Some thanked him for having saved their lives. "Everywhere I go people thank me for saving their lives," he said; "I don't know why they do it. I didn't do anything; Nature makes penicillin, I just found it."

In Oklahoma perspiring crowds of "city greeters" waited two hours to welcome him. His aircraft was due in at about half past five but only arrived two hours later, yet nobody went home. "As the little grey-haired man walked down the ramp," says a local newspaper report, "wearing a suit that was little darker than his tanned face, Oklahoma put its best foot forward. The governor was there, the mayor, leading business men and doctors. Thirty members of the Kilties band struck up their strange Scottish music.

" ' Everybody is hunting through microbes,' he told them with a smile, ' we'll have lots of nice things in the future.' " It had not taken him long to win them over, tired though he was by the rigours of his tour, by abundant hospitality and incessant receptions.

Sometimes he managed to steal a few moments of precious anonymity. At Madison Square Garden in New York he watched the boxing and " almost nobody in the crowd knew he was there and nobody asked him for his autograph." He slipped unnoticed into Chicago, thankfully, to address a meeting of doctors. Commenting on the visit a newspaperman said:

" Last week-end one of the world's really great men was in Chicago. He may have been responsible for saving the life of someone very dear to you. There is a possibility that he has figured in the saving of many more lives than this nation will lose in the war. But did crowds gather where they might see this man whose name will be in history? Did the bobby-soxers get hysterical around him? Did the autograph-seekers poke paper and pencil at him? Did the hotels go out of their way to fix him up with a fancy suite big enough for a rodeo? Were there any parades or any welcome signs in the windows?

" The answer is no.

" For which the really great man would be profoundly grateful, had the possibility of this nuisance occurred to him. The really great man is Sir Alexander Fleming, the small white-haired Scotch scientist who discovered penicillin.

"About the only indication of spontaneous public recognition of Sir Alexander's tremendous service to man came from a burly park policeman when Dr. Morris Fishbein was piloting Sir Alexander at the Rosenwald Museum.

" The policeman, learning the identity of Fishbein's passenger, said : ' I'd like to shake the hand of the man who has been such a great benefactor to humanity.'

" Maybe this all goes to show that our sense of comparative values is pretty low and is a primary reason for the troubles that beset us."

Harvard University gave him the degree of Doctor of Science, and he was the first foreign citizen to get the United States Medal for Merit. " The exigencies of war," he always told them, " have forced Britain and America to work together

and co-operate, and with the coming of peace it is hoped that
we will continue to work together for the benefit of all the
human race."

When he visited the Mayo Clinic, Dr. D. C. Balfour movingly
acknowledged the glowing climax of Fleming's work, all he had
done during those lonely hours in his laboratory extending over
a lifetime :

> " We have been eagerly awaiting your visit. Now that you
> are here, sir, may I say that informal as this occasion is, we trust
> you will feel it represents a tribute to you of the staff of the
> Clinic and the Faculty of the Mayo Foundation.
> "Although we know that wherever you may go in the world
> the highest honours would be accorded you for what your
> research has done for medical science and for humanity, we feel
> particularly indebted to you for your advice and counsel to
> those here who have had the responsibility of investigating the
> properties and clinical application of penicillin.
> " For this we shall be for ever grateful and any attempt to
> express in words our debt to you would be inadequate."

Perhaps the most magnificent formal occasion took place at
the Mayflower Hotel in Washington when he was presented
with the Variety Clubs' Humanitarian Award before members
of the Cabinet, the Diplomatic Corps and officers of the United
Nations, while the Secretary of the Treasury, Mr. Vinson read
out a letter from President Truman saying that the world
owed him a debt of gratitude difficult to estimate. It was a
sumptuous banquet, the apotheosis of fabulous American
hospitality. A report of it says :

> " Last week was one of the most memorable since the war
> began for the local *gourmets* who were lucky enough to be
> invited to the Variety Club Annual Humanitarian Award
> Banquet, in honour of Sir Alexander Fleming.
> " It was stag, unfortunately, but all the boys who could get
> to it in the midst of this mid-summer slump, found their general
> rain-soaked irritation dissipated when they sat down to what
> restrained observers reported was probably the most luscious
> banquet served here in several years.
> "At one point Mr. Butler, British Minister to Washington,
> who represented his absent chief, Lord Halifax, said he was
> taking the menu home to give it to his wife with the hope that
> she would be able to duplicate it ! He looked at the new
> Agricultural Secretary, Mr. Clinton P. Anderson, and added

with mock severity : ' I am assured by the Secretary of Agriculture that this will be possible.'

" The two hundred and fifty Cabinet, Senate and Diplomatic notables who gathered at the Mayflower ate turtle soup, followed by Imperial Crab, then the *pièce de resistance*, Breast of Capon —the plump white birds were all done up with *paté de foie gras* and mushrooms trussed inside. Vegetables were rissole potatoes and baby Lima beans, and the salad was of tomatoes and Avocado with a chestnut dressing. Ice cream larded with whipped cream and a rich strawberry sauce was served with *petit four* and *demitasse* for dessert, and there was so much enthusiasm for the food that at times during dinner the ball-room was almost golden with silence. What distinguished the menu was not only the essential splendour of the selections but the *cordon bleu* preparation of the food.

" Our banquet-goers have become so accustomed to the array of cold, pasty, cream-chicken or leathery fish, with assiduously green and bullet-like peas, that this culinary magnificence was almost too much for them.

" Whether inspired by food or drink, every one had a supremely gay evening and our statesmen were in fine form.

" There seems to have been a substantially impressive Kentucky delegation and the Texans were for once eclipsed.

" Senator Barkley said that after spending so many years watching a variety show up on the Senate floor, it was a pleasure to be around at a *bona fide* one !

"After dinner and a long evening of speeches and horse-play, the ranking guests departed and the Variety Club people, local and national theatre moguls, were sitting around upstairs having a peaceful nightcap when there was a knock at their door and they opened it to the gentle, unassuming award-winner, Sir Alexander, who stood clutching his plaque under his arm and said shyly that he wanted to tell them all what a good time he had had. He came in and sat around talking with them until five in the morning."

Meanwhile, in London, Menuhin played to more than six thousand people at the Albert Hall, at a concert organized by the *Daily Telegraph*, which raised over £5000 for further research into the uses of penicillin. The London Symphony Orchestra was conducted by a Frenchman, Paul Paray, and Menuhin played a Bach Violin Concerto in E Major, the Beethoven Violin Concerto and the Vieuxtemps in D Minor. At the end the audience refused to go home and stood clapping, cheering and stamping their feet until he hushed them with a transcription of a Bach Chaconne for the violin.

Returning home in August 1945, Fleming was soon to learn that he had been chosen Nobel Laureate in Medicine, the first selection since 1939. The prizes in wartime had been for those who could kill men in battle and now that the war was over it seemed like a favourable omen, for Nobel awards are associated with peace, and his aim had always been to preserve life not to destroy it. As Thomas Parran, Surgeon-General of the United States, had said : " Science has shown itself to be no respecter of life, note the V1, the V2 and other terrible weapons. It is very fortunate that we have men like Fleming who love life."

In September he set out for Paris to tell the *Académie de Médicine* about his discovery of penicillin, as Pasteur himself and other illustrious men had once told of their discoveries, and to receive the Legion of Honour.

On December 11th, 1945, in Stockholm, he delivered his Nobel Lecture on Penicillin, and recounting his recent experiences in America, he added : " To me it was of especial interest to see how a simple observation made in a hospital bacteriological laboratory in London had eventually developed into a large industry, and how what every one at one time thought was merely one of my toys had, by purification, become the nearest approach to the ideal substance for curing many of our common infections."

But as though to offset the pomp and circumstance, and to show that he was a simple man who belonged to simpler worlds, there is Miss Margaret Goldsmith's story of her visit to the Penicillin Exhibition at St. Mary's Hospital in the summer of 1945, told in her book, *The Road to Penicillin*. As she approached a closed door off a staircase on the way to the exhibition, the Secretary of the Hospital informed her : " In that room Professor Fleming discovered penicillin." There was a white card on the door bearing a handwritten inscription. But that inscription had no reference whatsoever to the greatest therapeutic discovery of the age. Instead it read : " Cat in residence."

In October 1943 Fleming had written to his friend, Ronald Gray, telling him how he had received a letter of congratulation from the council of his native village, Darvel. At the time he had replied to that letter from Darvel saying :

" I am in receipt of your letter, for which I thank you. Will you please convey to the Provost and Council my thanks for their congratulations. It is gratifying to think that my small efforts have been worthy of such an honour.

" It is not often now that I get to Darvel, but my heart is still with you and with the moors beyond."

The sequel to this exchange followed three years later. On Saturday, October 26th, 1946, just before three o'clock in the afternoon, Fleming stepped out of the car which had brought him to Darvel from Glasgow, to be received by the Provost, Magistrates, Town Councillors and burgh officials. With him were his wife, their only son, Robert, and his brother and sister-in-law, Mr. and Mrs. Robert Fleming.

In the main street the flags and the bunting rose and fell in a gusty breeze, the signals of greeting were everywhere, especially before the flag-swept Town Hall and municipal buildings where the burgh band played, and the news-reel camera-men and photographers stood waiting. Soon there was the skirl of pipes as the town pipers swung into view.

Fleming and his party went into the hall, hopelessly over-crowded, and took their places on the platform. Crowds gathered in the square outside to listen to the speeches relayed from within by a system of loud-speakers.

After the introductions, the Town Clerk read out the Burgess Ticket which constituted Sir Alexander Fleming a Burgess of the Burgh of Darvel and its first freeman :

BURGH OF DARVEL

At Darvel on the twenty-sixth day of October in the year one thousand nine hundred and forty-six, which day the Provost Magistrates, and Councillors of the Burgh of Darvel, being convened, they receive and admit :—

SIR ALEXANDER FLEMING,
M.B., B.S. (LOND.), F.R.C.S., F.R.C.P., F.R.S.,

to be a Burgess of the said Burgh, with the whole liberties, privileges and immunities thereto belonging ; in testimony of their high appreciation of the valuable service rendered by him to mankind by his scientific and medical research culminating in his discovery of Penicillin, and in appreciation of the ties of birthright existing between him and the Burgh of Darvel, and of the esteem and admiration which they hold for him personally.

This Burgess Ticket took the form of an illuminated scroll in which the lettering was done in red, black and gold, with the burgh coat-of-arms in blue and gold on the top left hand corner. The burnished casket or container for it was designed and made by a local craftsman, and the wood base bore an inscription-plate.

When he spoke to them, Fleming recalled the scenes of his boyhood, the house in the midst of the windswept moorlands in which he had been born, the tonic airs, the guddling for trout in the Glen Water, the hunt for peewits' eggs, the long climbs, the things learned from wild Nature :

> " It always seemed a pity that people want to get into towns. We have to live on the country. It is in the fields that our food is grown and if the process of migration were ever complete it might be a little awkward. But it will never be complete, for although the man in the country may have to work harder for his money, he has got a man's life, he does not need to do the same thing day after day. He has got variety in his work, and he has Nature all around him."

He had been to the " wee school out in the country away beyond Darvel where they really taught you something " (the school house had come up for sale and had been bought by the Fleming family) ; he had been to Darvel School and then he had been to Kilmarnock Academy, " a very good school, a very big school on the top of a hill ". He scanned the upturned faces in front of him :

> " There will be many in your midst who went to school with me. I am afraid I cannot recognize you now."

London had taken him ; the favours of fortune had shone down upon him, he had found penicillin :

> " It is the glory of a good bit of work that it opens the way for better things and thus rapidly leads to its own eclipse. The object of research is the advancement not of the investigator, but of knowledge."

Yet this very countryside had borne him :

> " I have not been in this countryside except for a few days now and then for many years. The people change, man-made

things change, but the country is just the same. The same pools are in the burn, the same stones are there ; and I have no doubt the same trout we guddled as boys are under the same stones. It is all the same except for the human difference."

He was back again among his very " ain folk ", his heart still with them and with the moors beyond.

CHAPTER XVII

" . . . THE FLAVOUR OF YOUTH "

THE NEXT years streamed by, Fleming stood within the dazzling light of universal renown, widely demanded on all sides, but the bright public life was to be darkened by a private grief. Despite the distractions, he remained stubbornly anchored to his work. " Contentment and smug satisfaction find no culture plate for themselves within the mind of the great scientist " said an observer. To old friends he was still the same, they saw him unchanged, his loyalties intact, and without exception they could speak of him with all their old affection.

Events picked out at random from these crowded years show the man himself as he participates in them with zest.

September 1947 : Attends the International Conference of Physicians in London, and the Twelfth International Congress of the International Society of Surgery. Also awarded the John Scott Medal in Philadelphia, which is accepted for him in his absence by Lord Halifax, British Ambassador to the United States. John Scott was an Edinburgh chemist who left a large trust fund in that city so that men of science might be honoured.

In 1947, Sir Almroth Wright, his master and friend died in his eighty-seventh year. Theirs had been a long, affectionate and fruitful association ; it was for Fleming a saddening moment. Happily Wright had been spared to see the triumph of penicillin.

June 1948 : Writes to his friend Ronald Gray : " We have just returned from three hectic weeks in Spain."

Tells another friend, Robin Bailes, how at a banquet in that country they set before him a tasty dish of pigs' trotters, ' a dish I know and like as a countryman '. He tucked in with relish, to find with dismay that many courses were yet to come. Heroically he fought his way through the whole menu so as not to offend his kind hosts.

August 1949 : " I had a marvellous time in America and afterwards in Verona " he writes again to Gray. " I will tell you about it some time. Meanwhile I hope you are enjoying yourself and doing some of your wonderful water-colours."

Signor Eugenio Bertuetti, who had been with him during the Verona Medical Congress has set down some attractive impressions of him :

" We are guests at a beautiful, hospitable house at Valeggio on the Mincio. . . . An enormous park, thick with oaks and cypresses and myrtles that were centuries old, with slightly sloping meadows here and there, crowned by a wood on the hill-top and crossed by Virgil's lazy and blue Mincio.

" Beneath a majestic oak, big enough to fill a cathedral there is a tiny man in a hazy double-breasted suit with the rosette of the *Legion d'Honneur* in his button hole, and the charming garnet red, white-dotted bow tie. Above the square lenses of his spectacles his eyes, milky-blue like those of a newly born kitten's, stare intently at people with whom he converses ; his solid, sun-tanned forehead is topped with snow-white, thick shining hair . . . one cannot refrain from thinking of the terrific spiritual power concealed within this unassuming little man.

" Somebody tells him : ' Please excuse us, Sir Alexander, if we are a bit confused and shy when we are in your presence.' To which he replies : ' Nobody could be more confused or shy than I myself. . . .' "

" When they ask him whether he would like to swim in the pool, he says : ' Yes, with pleasure.' Maybe he likes water best among the beauties of Nature, for he seems to own this lively element, when he dives into it with the mastery of an athlete. And Fleming is sixty-eight. . . .

Two little girls, the small daughters of a famous European lung surgeon, Professor Brunner of Zürich, chase him through the waters, " a tiny Triton who was trying to escape, hanging on to a small canoe and desperately working the paddle. At that moment all in him was the child, his movements were those of a child, his leaps, his smiles and his full-throated laughs as he managed to get safely past his assailants. They, however, finally reached the small boat and overturned it with joyful shouts. The poor Triton went to the bottom, only to pop up again, blinded and dripping and spluttering, amid the mocking laughter of the two children. . . ."

When Fleming arrived for a gala evening on the shores of Lake Garda, " mixed up with the doctors were a throng of other people who had nothing to do with medicine : boys, girls, parents with their children. . . . All of a sudden a man in shirt sleeves came out of the throng and stepped towards him, surrounded by his three children who knelt beside him. ' If these children are alive·' he said, ' they owe it to you.'

" Fleming glanced up and smiled. Suddenly a photographer in the darkness shot off his flash-bulb.

" The man told his three sons to get up and pointing to Fleming told them : ' Never forget to ask God in your prayers to bless this man. . . .' "

September 1949 : He returns from Italy and is distressed to find his wife is in poor health. " I found her very ill and she has been for the whole of August in the private wing of the hospital. Soon she will be coming back but it will be some time before she is able to go to the country."

Summer 1950 : He and Robin Bailes go down to Bisley to fire for the Masonic Gavel, an inter-masonic lodge shooting competition. They are firing for the London Scottish team. On the Saturday they go out for some practice ; Fleming is back at the sport he had loved and in which he had excelled. " This is the first time I've fired at Bisley for twenty-five years " he said as he took up his rifle. Perhaps he had not made enough allowance for recoil, but it kicked back, hitting him on the bridge of the nose and throwing off his glasses, leaving a nasty cut.
He wiped off the blood with his handkerchief and went on firing but performed indifferently.
That evening there was a general reunion, and though he is abstemious, he stayed up till one o'clock in the morning playing darts and joining in the fun.
On the Sunday he went out to fire in the competition proper and returned top score for his side.

August 1950 : A journey to Rio de Janeiro. He writes : " That gave us some excitements for we were three hours out over the Atlantic when one of the engines failed and we had to turn back to Africa on three engines and get the other repaired before we set out again. When we got to Rio, they housed the whole Congress—about five hundred—in an enormous hotel in the mountains where the climate was perfect.
" I really had a good time, but I was too much feted."

Within three weeks he is in Rome where he pays another visit to the Pope. " There was too much fuss " he observes, " but they were very kind. . . . Since I returned from Rome in September, I have been quietly at home, but on November 24th I go to Brussels for two days. It is the eightieth birthday of a famous bacteriologist (Jules Bordet), and I have to make a speech of about fifteen minutes *in French* on behalf of the foreign scientists.
" I hope they understand it."

April 1951 : " I am off to Pakistan for ten days. . . ."

He is an Honorary Freeman of his native Darvel, of the Borough of Paddington where he has worked all his life, of the Borough of Chelsea where he has lived so many years, and of Verona in Italy. In Paddington he has also opened Fleming Court, a large block of flats named after him, he is an Honorary Chief of the Doy-gei-taun of Kiowa tribe, a member of the Pontifical Academy of Sciences, and has the Grand Cross of Alphonse the Wise of Spain. . . .

To his pleasure, his son has followed in his footsteps and qualified as a doctor.

But the brilliance of his life and of his achievements are dimmed at the zenith : his wife, after a tragic illness is dead and he is alone. Yet happily she had been with him to share his triumphant moments, as she had shared with him the lesser times. And in his work there is everlasting consolation, for in it he has found both beauty and truth among the disappointments which he had faced with the rugged stoicism in his nature.

" I have still got a few useful years before me " he said on his seventieth birthday, August 6th, 1951, and to those who wanted to be well and happy he offered the old advice : " Keep on working."

For all his years, he is still to be seen in the Wright-Fleming Institute of Microbiology, striding its long corridor with springy step, with signs of energy that would be enviable in a far younger man. Watching him there come to mind some lines of Cicero's :

> " Just as I approve of a young man in whom there is a touch of age, so I approve of the old man in whom there is some of the flavour of youth. He who strives thus to mingle youthfulness and age may grow old in body, but old in spirit he never will be. . . ."

BIBLIOGRAPHY

SIR ALEXANDER FLEMING
M.B., B.S. (LOND.), F.R.C.S., F.R.C.P., F.R.S.

PUBLICATIONS

1908. THE PRACTITIONER
Some observations on the Opsonic Index, with special reference to the accuracy of the method and to some of the sources of error.

1908. THE LANCET
The accuracy of Opsonic estimations.

1909. ST. MARY'S HOSPITAL GAZETTE
The Diagnosis of Acute Bacterial Infections.

1909. ST. MARY'S HOSPITAL GAZETTE
Acute Bacterial Infections.

1909. TRANSACTIONS OF THE MEDICAL SOCIETY OF LONDON.
Serum Diagnosis of Syphilis by a Simple Modification of Wassermann's Method.

1909. THE LANCET
The Eiology of Acne Vulgaris and Its Treatment by Vaccines.

1909. THE LANCET
Simple Method of Serum Diagnosis of Syphilis.

1911. THE LANCET
The Use of Salvarsan in the treatment of Syphilis.

1915. THE LANCET
On the Bacteriology of Septic Wounds.

1917. THE LANCET
Studies in Wound Infections.

1917. THE LANCET
The Physiological and Antiseptic Action of Flavine.

1918. THE LANCET
Acidæmia in gas-gangrene, and on the conditions which favour the growth of its infective agent in the blood fluids.

1918. THE LANCET
A case of rat-bite fever.

BIBLIOGRAPHY

1918. THE LANCET
> The Sterilisation of Wounds by Physiological Agency.

1919. THE LANCET
> Streptococcal Infections of Septic Wounds at a Base Hospital.

1919. THE LANCET
> On some simply prepared culture media for B. Influenzæ.

1919. THE LANCET
> An experimental research into the specificity of the agglutinins produced by Pfeiffer's bactillus.

1919. THE LANCET
> Blood Transfusion by the Citrate Method.

1919. THE BRITISH JOURNAL OF SURGERY
> The Action of Chemical and Physiological Antiseptics in a Septic Wound.

1920. THE BRITISH JOURNAL OF EXPERIMENTAL PATHOLOGY
> Method of automatically recording gas produced by bacteria.

1921. THE BRITISH JOURNAL OF EXPERIMENTAL PATHOLOGY
> On the Antigenic Properties of Acetone-extracted Bacteria.

1922. THE BRITISH JOURNAL OF EXPERIMENTAL PATHOLOGY
> Observations on a Bacteriolytic Substance (Lysozyme) found in secretions and tissues.

1922. PROCEEDINGS OF THE ROYAL SOCIETY
> On a Remarkable Bacteriolytic Element found in Tissues and Secretions.

1922. PROCEEDINGS OF THE ROYAL SOCIETY
> Further Observations on a Bacteriolytic Element found in Tissues and Secretions.

1924. THE LANCET
> On the Antibacterial Power of Egg-white.

1924. PROCEEDINGS OF THE ROYAL SOCIETY
> A Comparison of the Activities of Antiseptics on Bacteria and on Leucocytes.

1925. BRITISH JOURNAL OF EXPERIMENTAL PATHOLOGY
> On the Specificity of the Protein of human tears.

1926. BRITISH JOURNAL OF EXPERIMENTAL PATHOLOGY
> The Effect of Variations on the Salt content of Blood on its Bactericidal Power in Vitro and In Vivo.

BIBLIOGRAPHY

1926. BRITISH JOURNAL OF EXPERIMENTAL PATHOLOGY
Simple Method of Removing Leucocytes from Blood.

1927. BRITISH JOURNAL OF EXPERIMENTAL PATHOLOGY
On Wright's Centrifuge Method of Estimating Phagocytosis and the Rate of Opsonisation of Bacteria by Normal Serum.

1927. BRITISH JOURNAL OF EXPERIMENTAL PATHOLOGY
The Development of Strains of Bacteria Resistant to Lysozyme Action and the Relation of Lysozyme Action to Intracellular Digestion.

1928. BRITISH JOURNAL OF EXPERIMENTAL PATHOLOGY
On the Influence of Temperature on the Rate of Agglutination of Bacteria.

1928. PROCEEDINGS OF THE ROYAL SOCIETY OF MEDICINE
The Bactericidal Power of Human Blood and Some Methods of Altering it.

1928. BRITISH JOURNAL OF EXPERIMENTAL PATHOLOGY
On the Antibacterial Action of Cultures of a Penicillium with special reference to their use in the isolation of B. Influenzæ.

1929. THE LANCET
Arris and Gale Lecture. Lysozyme.

1930. BRITISH JOURNAL OF EXPERIMENTAL PATHOLOGY
On the Occurrence of Influenzæ Bacilli in the Mouths of Normal People.

1931. THE BRITISH DENTAL JOURNAL
Some Problems in the Use of Antiseptics.

1931. PROCEEDINGS OF THE ROYAL SOCIETY OF MEDICINE
The Intravenous use of Germicides.

1932. PROCEEDINGS OF THE ROYAL SOCIETY OF MEDICINE
Lysozyme.

1932. JOURNAL OF STATE MEDICINE
The Trend of Modern Research in Bacteriology.

1932. JOURNAL OF PATHOLOGY AND BACTERIOLOGY
On the Specific Antibacterial Properties of Penicillin and Potassium Tellurite.

1938. BRITISH MEDICAL JOURNAL
Treatment of Pneumonia.

1938. THE LANCET
The Antibacterial Action In Vitro of 2-(p-Aminobenzenesulphonamido) Pyridine on Pneumococci and Streptococci.

BIBLIOGRAPHY

1938. THE LANCET
The Antibacterial Power of the Blood of Patients Receiving 2-(p-Aminobenzenesulphonamido) Pyridine.

1939. BRITISH MEDICAL JOURNAL
Recent Advances in Vaccine Therapy.

1939. THE LANCET
M. & B. 693 and Pneumococci.

1939. PROCEEDINGS OF THE ROYAL SOCIETY OF MEDICINE
Serum and Vaccine Therapy in Combination with Sulphanilamide or M. & B. 693.

1940. WAR SURGERY (Hamilton BAILEY)
Bacteriological Examination of Wounds.

1940. MODERN TRENDS IN OPHTHALMOLOGY
Chemotherapy in Ophthamology.

1940 PROCEEDINGS OF THE ROYAL SOCIETY OF MEDICINE
The Effects of Antiseptics on Wounds.

1940. JOURNAL OF PATHOLOGY AND BACTERIOLOGY
Observations on the Bacteriostatic Action of Sulphanilamide and M & B 693 and on the Influence thereon of Bacteria and Peptone.

1940. JOURNAL OF PATHOLOGY AND BACTERIOLOGY
The Inhibitory Action of Potassium Tellurite on Coliform Bacteria.

1941. THE LANCET
A pneumococcus which required CO_2 for its Growth.

1941. PROCEEDINGS OF THE ROYAL SOCIETY OF MEDICINE
Chemotherapy and Wound Infection.

1941. JOURNAL OF PATHOLOGY AND BACTERIOLOGY
Some Uses of Nigrosin in Bacteriology.

1942. BRITISH MEDICAL JOURNAL
Simple Method of Using Penicillin, Tellurite and Gentian Violet for Differential Culture.

1942. BIOCHEMICAL JOURNAL
The Mode of Action of Chemotherapeutic Agents.

1942. THE LANCET
In Vitro Tests of Penicillin Potency.

1943. PROCEEDINGS OF THE ROYAL SOCIETY OF MEDICINE
Active Immunity—General Considerations.

BIBLIOGRAPHY

1943.—THE LANCET
Streptococcal Meningitis treated with Penicillin.

1943. PROCEEDINGS OF THE LINNEAN SOCIETY OF LONDON
The Use of Paper and Cellophane Discs for the Preparation of Museum Specimens of Mould Cultures.

1944. PROCEEDINGS OF THE ROYAL SOCIETY OF MEDICINE
Penicillin.

1944. TRANSACTIONS OF THE BRITISH MYCOLOGICAL SOCIETY
Some methods for the study of moulds.

1944. ULSTER MEDICAL JOURNAL
The Robert Campbell Oration—Penicillin.

1944. Lister Memorial Lecture—Antiseptics.

1944. JOURNAL OF THE ROYAL INSTITUTE OF PUBLIC HEALTH
AND HYGIENE
Harben Lecture—Penicillin—Its Discovery, Development and Uses in the Field of Medicine and Surgery.

1945. PROCEEDINGS OF THE STAFF MEETINGS OF THE MAYO CLINIC
Antiseptics, Old and New.

1946. Linacre Lecture-Chemotherapy, Yesterday, Today and Tomorrow.

1947. THE LANCET
Estimation of Penicillin in Serum.   Use of Glucose, Phenol Red and Serum Water.

1947. BRITISH MEDICAL JOURNAL
Louis Pasteur.

1947. BRITISH MEDICAL JOURNAL
Influence of Penicillin on the Coagulation of Blood.
The Role of Penicillin in Surgical Practice.

1946. BUTTERWORTH'S MEDICAL PUBLICATIONS
Penicillin—Its Practical Application.

1950. JOURNAL OF GENERAL MICROBIOLOGY
The Morphology and Motility of Proteus Vulgaris and Other Organisms cultured in the Presence of Penicillin.

1950. JOURNAL OF GENERAL MICROBIOLOGY
Further Observations on the Motility of Proteus Vulgaris Grown on Penicillin Agar.

1950. MEDICINE ILLUSTRATED
Antibiotic Therapy.

BIBLIOGRAPHY

1950. THE PRACTITIONER
       Current Therapeutics, Modern Penicillin Therapy.

1950. ANNALES DE L'INSTITUT PASTEUR
       Hommage à Jules Bordet au nom des Savants Etrangers.

1951. BRITISH MEDICAL JOURNAL
       Syringe needles and mass inoculation technique.

I have made no attempt to list here the many books and periodicals I have consulted, but content myself with mentioning certain works which deal with the history of penicillin. They are:

THE STORY OF PENICILLIN
    George Lacken (Pilot Press, 1945).

MIRACLE DRUG
    David Masters (Eyre & Spottiswoode, 1946).

THE ROAD TO PENICILLIN
    Margaret Goldsmith (Lindsay Drummond, 1946).

PENICILLIN
    Boris Sokoloff (Allen & Unwin, 1946).

Mr. Chapman Pincher's " Four-Point Scale " (p. 124) appeared in an article in the *Daily Express*.

INDEX

AIRD, Martha, 21
Allison, Dr. V. D., 99–101
Anderson, Clinton P., 204
Appleton, Sir Edward, 109

BAILES, Robin, 26, 51–2, 66, 210, 212
Balfour, A. J., 46
Balfour, Dr. D. C., 204
Barkley, Senator, 196, 205
Bateman, H. M., 15
Beerbohm, Max, 53
Bertuetti, Eugenio, 211
Biochemical Journal, The, 146
Biourge, 136
Bordet, Prof. Jules, 60, 106, 212
British Journal of Experimental Pathology, The, 136, 147, 172
British Journal of Surgery, The, 79
British Medical Journal, The, 164
Brunner, Prof., 211
Burns, Robert, 25, 111
Butler, R. A., 204

CAIRNS, Mary (*née* Morton), 27
Cameron, Sir John, 183
Carmalt Jones, David, 31–2, 45, 46, 63, 68
Chain, Dr. E. B., 171, 172, 173–7, 180
Chelsea Arts Club, The, 54, 122, 131
Cheyne, Sir William Watson, 79, 80
Churchill, Rt. Hon. W. S., 15, 189, 196
Cicero, M. Tullius, 213
Clemenger, Lt. Col. Francis J., 94–5
Coghill, Dr. R. D., 177, 183
Colebrook, Dr. Leonard, 32, 35, 42–3, 44, 46, 49, 55, 61, 63, 64, 68, 75, 79
Collitti, Dr., 191
Craig, Peter, 23
Curie, Marie, 125
Cushing, Dr. Harvey, 82

DAILY GRAPHIC, The, 49
Daily Telegraph, The, 205
Darvel, 18–25, 27, 206–9
Darvel School, 22–4, 208
Darwin, C. R., 110
Destin des Maladies Infectieuses, 123–4
" Dhoon, The," 122, 200
Disraeli, Benjamin, 18

Doctor's Dilemma, The, 36–7, 73
Domagh, Dr. Gerhardt, 158–9
Douglas, Dr. S. R., 34, 75
Dubos, Dr. Réné J., 111
Duclaux, 44
Duncan, Sir Andrew, 182

EHRLICH, Dr. Paul, 46, 61–2, 119, 155, 157, 161–2, 185, 192, 199
Einstein, Albert, 109
Emmerich, Dr., 141

FISHBEIN, Dr. Morris, 203
Fisher, H. A. L., 51, 82
Fleming, Sir Alexander : birth of, 18; boyhood and education in Scotland, 20–5 ; moves to London, 26 ; at Regent Street Polytechnic, 27 ; joins shipping company, 28 ; joins London Scottish Volunteers, 29 ; decides to take up medicine, 30 ; at St. Mary's Hospital Medical School, 33 ff. ; qualifies in Medicine and Joins Wright's laboratory, 40 ; his technical skill, 43 ; and early clinical experience, 43–7 ; publishes his first paper, 48 ; his success in shooting at Bisley, 49–50 ; sits for his M.B., B.S. Examination, 50 ; joins Chelsea Arts Club, 54 ; his interest in art, 54–5 ; becomes a Freemason, 56 ; his researches into Vaccines, 58–9 ; into Syphilis, 59–60 ; his experiments with and paper on Salvarsan, 61–2 ; leaves the London Scottish Regiment, 66 ; joins R.A.M.C. Unit under Wright at Boulogne, 68 ; works with wounded, 68–81 ; his researches into antiseptics and wound infection, 69–73; demobilized, 82 ; delivers Hunterian Lecture before Royal College of Surgeons, 84 ; his research into and papers on Leucocytes, 86–91 ; discovers Lysozyme, 97 ; publications on Lysozyme, 97–107 : delivers Presidential Address to the Royal Society of Medicine, 103 : his marriage, 108 ; further researches into Bacteriology and Antiseptics, 114–6 ; his mother's death, 122 ;

INDEX

Fleming, Sir Alexander
appointed Professor of Bacteriology in University of London, 122 ; buys house in Suffolk, 122 ; discovers penicillin, 131 ff. ; his first researches into, 134–5 ; his first paper on, 136–7 ; his early clinical tests with, 138–44 ; uses penicillin for bacteriological research, 149–51 ; investigates Prontosil and sulfa drugs, 159–68 ; tests the first stable penicillin produced at Oxford, 176 ; treats his first patient with stable penicillin, 181 ; attends conference with Ministry of Supply, 182 ; continues research into properties and powers of penicillin, 185 ; emphasises its limitations, 192–4 ; elected Fellow of the Royal Society, 200 ; knighted, 201 ; visits U.S.A., 202–5 ; honoured by Harvard University, 203 ; visits the Mayo Clinic, 204 ; honoured by the Variety Clubs of America, 204–5 ; awarded Nobel Prize for Medicine, 206 ; lectures to Académie de Médicine, 206 ; presented the freedom of Darvel, 206–9; his travels and honours, 210–3.

Fleming, Grace (*née* Morton), 19–20, 122.

Fleming, Grace, 19, 20, 28
Fleming, Hugh, 19–20
Fleming, Hugh, jr., 19, 20
Fleming, Jean, 19, 28
Fleming, John, 19, 20, 22, 26, 28–9, 108
Fleming, Mary, 19, 28
Fleming, Robert, 19, 20, 21, 22, 23, 24, 26, 28–9, 32, 207
Fleming, Robert, jr., 122, 207
Fleming, Sarah (*née* McElroy), 108, 122, 189, 207
Fleming, Thomas, 19, 26, 28, 111
Florey, Sir Howard, 107, 171, 172, 173–82, 186, 198, 202
Förster, Dr., 158
Freeman, John, 46, 55, 68

Gelmo, Paul, 158
Gladstone, W. E., 18
Glasgow University, 26
Goldsmith, Margaret, 206
Gorrie, 23
Grant, Col. Lyall, 29–30
Gray, Ronald, 15, 52–5, 113, 200, 206, 210
Guedella, Philip, 190

Haeckel, Ernst, 110
Halifax, Lord, 204, 210
Harvard University, 203
Heatley, Dr. N. G., 177
Herrell, Dr. Wallace E., 96, 136, 143
Hunter, John, 112
Huxley, Aldous, 125, 142
Huxley, T. H., 110

James, William, 81
Jenner, Edward, 65, 185
Joad, Prof. C. E. M., 110
Johnson, Dr., 110
Jones, N. Howard, 160

Keefer, Chester, 183, 191
Keith, Dr. N. M., 83, 108–9, 168
Kilmarnock Academy, 24–5, 208
Kipling, Rudyard, 196
Koch, Robert, 33, 46, 185

Lancet, The, 47, 58, 59, 61, 74, 80, 174, 175, 185
Lister, Lord, 57, 69–70, 73, 79, 126, 185, 195
Lister Institute, The, 146
Lochfield Farm,18–25, 26, 27
London School of Hygiene and Tropical Medicine, The, 137, 145, 152
London Scottish Volunteers, The, 26, 29–30, 49–50, 66
Loudoun Moor School, 20–2
Löw, Dr., 141
Ludwig, K. F. W., 40
Lysozyme, 13, 97 ff., 108, 126, 130, 133, 171–2

M & B (Sulphapyridine), 157, 165, 167–8, 170
Maclean, Dr., 150, 167
Malone, Patricia, 191–2
Masters, David, 171
Mayo Clinic, The, 83, 96, 108, 127, 136, 143, 168, 183, 204
Medical Research Council, The, 132
Menuhin, Yehudi, 205
Metalnikov, Dr. Serge, 39
Metchnikov, Elie, 33, 34, 63, 105, 162
Miracle Drug, 171–2
Moore, George, 52
Montaigne, M. de, 108
Montgomery of Alamein, Viscount, 188
Moran, Lord, 32, 110, 185, 187
Morgan, Parry, 46, 68

NEWTON, Sir Isaac, 83, 110, 124, 200
New York Journal-American, The, 190–1
Nicolle, Dr. Charles, 123
Noon, Dr. Leonard, 44, 46, 47, 55

PAINE, Dr. C. G., 147–8
Pannett, Prof. Charles, 32, 45, 47, 66, 68–9, 92, 106
Paracelsus, 154, 163
Paray, Paul, 205
Park, Dr., 95
Parran, Thomas, 196, 206
Pasteur, Louis, 13, 15, 16, 19, 35, 42, 44, 57, 62, 63, 64, 65, 69–70, 96, 111, 112, 120, 129, 134, 152, 155, 161, 196, 206
Penicillin : discovery, 131–4 ; first investigations by Fleming, 134–6 ; his first paper on, 136–9 ; his first clinical tests, 141 ; chemical investigations of, by Raistrick *et al.*, 145–7 ; clinical tests by Paine, 147–9 ; used in bacteriological research by Fleming, 149 – 53 ; investigation taken up by Florey and Chain, 172 ; the Oxford experiments and the stabilisation of penicillin, 173–7 ; manufacture commenced in U.S.A., 177 ; first clinical use in U.S.A., 178 ; manufacture in Britain, 179–80 ; used clinically by Fleming, 180–1 ; Committee of Manufacture formed, 182 ; commercially exploitation of, 183 ; described in *The Times,* 184 ; use on war casualties, 185–8 ; used in the Patricia Malone case, 190–2 ; limitations pointed out by Fleming, 192–4 ; formula for, 195
Pennsylvania University, 145
Pfeiffer, Emil, 33, 94–5
Pincher, Chapman, 124–7, 142
Practitioner, The, 48
Proceedings of the Royal Society of Medicine, 114
Prontosil, 158–9, 161
Punch, 155

RAISTRICK, Prof. Harold, 137, 145–7, 149, 151–2, 172, 173, 182
Regent Street Polytechnic, The, 27
Reid, 149
Richards, Dr. A. N., 183, 191
Road to Penicillin, The, 206
Rockefeller Foundation, The, 177
Rogers, Dr., 167

Ross, Sir Ronald, 199
Royal Society of Medicine, The, 79, 103, 117, 119, 175, 202
Russell, Bertrand, 39
Rutherford, Lord, 124

ST. MARY'S HOSPITAL, 11, 12, 15, 30, 31, 33, 41, 44, 48, 54, 55, 62, 63, 64, 68, 82, 94, 96, 99, 110, 122, 129, 146, 147, 152, 167, 172, 176, 180–1, 200, 206
St. Mary's Hospital Gazette, 56
Salvarsan (606), 61–2, 155, 161
Shaw, George Bernard, 36, 46, 73, 84, 116
Sickert, Walter, 53
Sokoloff, Dr. Boris, 162
Spilsbury, Bernard, 46
Stevenson, Robert Louis, 25
Stirling, Marion, 21
Sulphanilamide, 159 ff.

THOM, C., 137, 146, 177
Those Barren Leaves, 125
Times, The, 184, 201
Trefouels, Prof., 159
Trevelyan, G. M., 19
Truman, President, 204

UNIVERSITY OF LONDON, The, 122

VAN LEEUWENHOEK, Antony, 154, 155, 200
Variety Clubs of America, 15, 204–5
Victoria, Queen, 27
Vienna General Hospital, 15
Vinson, 204
von Behring, ——, 33

WELLS, Dr., 44
Whistler, J. A. M., 53, 200
Who's Who, 202
Wilde, Oscar, 53
Wood, Mrs. Eva, 197
Wright, Sir Almroth, 12–3, 14, 16, 30, 32, 33– 38, 40, 41, 42–7, 52, 53, 55, 57, 63, 64, 65, 66, 67–8, 73–4, 75–80, 82–3, 84–5, 93, 97, 101, 110, 114, 120, 123, 125, 134, 145, 155, 184, 199, 210
Wright, Dickson, 196
Wright-Fleming Institute of Microbiology, The, 14–6, 213